BIOL 2010

Microbiology Text Book

Adapted from OpenStax Microbiology

https://openstax.org/details/books/microbiology

Edited by Brenda Gustin, PhD
Corning Community College
1st Edition
11/2019

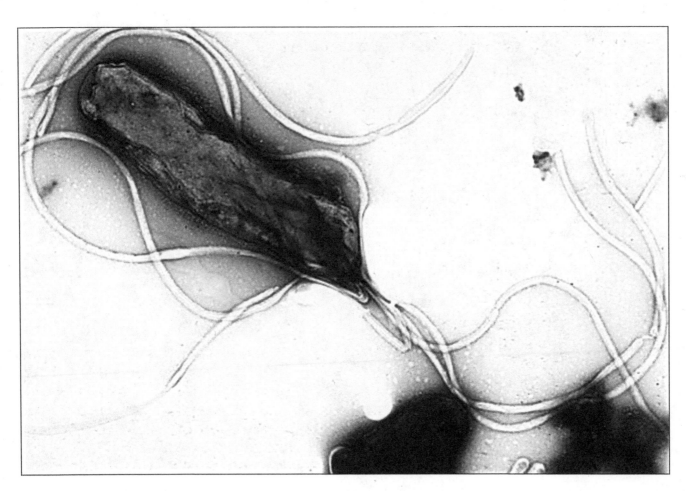

Helicobacter pylori can cause chronic gastritis, which can lead to ulcers and stomach cancer.

This text was originally published by OpenStax and can be accessed at https://openstax.org/details/books/microbiology

Microbiology BIOL 2010 was curated by Brenda Gustin at the State University of New York at Corning Community College in 2019.

Published by SUNY OER Services

SUNY Office of Library and Information Services
10 N Pearl St

Albany, NY 12207

Distributed by State University of New York Press

ISBN: 978-1-64176-070-6

Contents

Chemistry Review

Elements, Atoms, Molecules

The most abundant **element** in cells is hydrogen (H), followed by carbon (C), oxygen (O), nitrogen (N), phosphorous (P), and sulfur (S). We call these elements macronutrients, and they account for about 99% of the dry weight of cells. Some elements, such as sodium (Na), potassium (K), magnesium (Mg), zinc (Zn), iron (Fe), calcium (Ca), molybdenum (Mo), copper (Cu), cobalt (Co), manganese (Mn), or vanadium (V), are required by some cells in very small amounts and are called micronutrients or trace elements. All of these elements are essential to the function of many biochemical reactions, and, therefore, are essential to life. A single unit of a particular element is an **atom**. Atoms combine to produce **moleules.**

The four most abundant elements in living matter (C, N, O, and H) have low atomic numbers and are thus light elements capable of

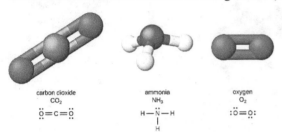

Figure 1. Some common molecules include carbon dioxide, ammonia, and oxygen, which consist of combinations of oxygen atoms (red spheres), carbon atoms (gray spheres), hydrogen atoms (white spheres), or nitrogen atoms (blue spheres).

forming strong bonds with other atoms to produce molecules. Carbon forms four chemical bonds, whereas nitrogen forms three, oxygen forms two, and hydrogen forms one. When bonded together within molecules, oxygen, sulfur, and nitrogen often have one or more "lone pairs" of electrons that play important roles in determining many of the molecules' physical and chemical properties. These traits in combination permit the formation of a vast number of diverse molecular species necessary to form the structures and enable the functions of living organisms.

Living organisms contain inorganic compounds (mainly water and salts; see and organic molecules. **Organic molecules** contain carbon and hydrogen; **inorganic molecules** do not. The atoms of an organic molecule are typically organized around chains of carbon atoms.

Inorganic compounds make up 1%–1.5% of the dry weight of living cells. They are small, simple compounds that play important roles in the cell, although they do not form cell structures. Most of the carbon found in organic molecules originates from inorganic carbon sources such as carbon dioxide captured via carbon fixation by microorganisms.

Organic Molecules

Carbon chains form the skeletons of most organic molecules. Functional groups combine with the chain to form biomolecules. Because these biomolecules are typically large, we call them **macromolecules**. Many biologically relevant macromolecules are formed by linking together a great number of identical, or very similar, smaller organic molecules. The smaller molecules act as building blocks and are called monomers, and the macromolecules that result from their linkage are called polymers. Cells and cell structures include four main groups of carbon-containing molecules: carbohydrates, proteins, lipids, and nucleic acids. The first three groups of molecules will be studied throughout this chapter. The nucleic acids will be discussed in more detail in the Genetics chapter.

Of the many possible ways that monomers may be combined to yield polymers, one common approach encountered in the formation of biological macromolecules is dehydration synthesis. In this chemical reaction, monomer molecules bind end to end in a process that results in the formation of water molecules as a byproduct:

H—monomer—OH+H—monomer—OH—monomer—monomer—OH+H2O

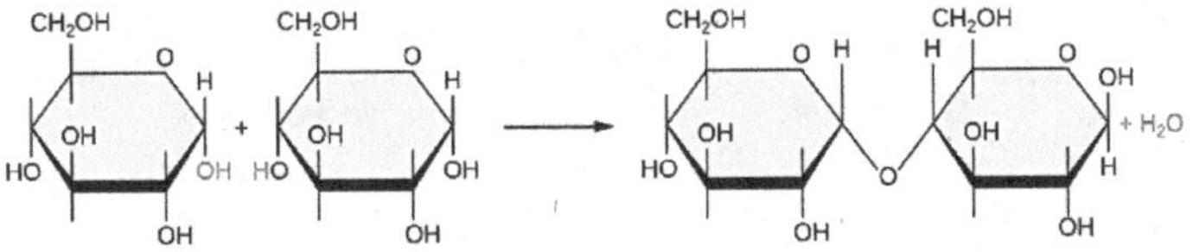

Figure 2. In this dehydration synthesis reaction, two molecules of glucose are linked together to form maltose. In the process, a water molecule is formed.

Some Functions of Macromolecules	
Macromolecule	**Functions**
Carbohydrates	Energy storage, receptors, food, structural role in plants, fungal cell walls, exoskeletons of insects
Lipids	Energy storage, membrane structure, insulation, hormones, pigments
Nucleic acids	Storage and transfer of genetic information
Proteins	Enzymes, structure, receptors, transport, structural role in the cytoskeleton of a cell and the extracellular matrix

Table 1

Introduction to Microbiology

From boiling thermal hot springs to deep beneath the Antarctic ice, microorganisms can be found almost everywhere on earth in great quantities. **Microorganisms** (or microbes, as they are also called) are small organisms. Most are so small that they cannot be seen without a microscope.

Most microorganisms are harmless to humans and, in fact, many are helpful. They play fundamental roles in ecosystems everywhere on earth, forming the backbone of many food webs. People use them to make biofuels, medicines, and even foods.

Without microbes, there would be no bread, cheese, or beer. Our bodies are filled with microbes, and our skin alone is home to trillions of them.[1] Some of them we can't live without; others cause diseases that can make us sick or even kill us.

Although much more is known today about microbial life than ever before, the vast majority of this invisible world remains unexplored. Microbiologists continue to identify new ways that microbes benefit and threaten humans.

Most people today, even those who know very little about microbiology, are familiar with the concept of microbes, or "germs," and their role in human health. Schoolchildren learn about bacteria, viruses, and other microorganisms, and many even view specimens under a microscope. But a few hundred years ago, be-

Figure 1 A veterinarian gets ready to clean a sea turtle covered in oil following the Deepwater Horizon oil spill in the Gulf of Mexico in 2010. After the spill, the population of a naturally occurring oil-eating marine bacterium called Alcanivorax borkumensis skyrocketed, helping to get rid of the oil. Scientists are working on ways to genetically engineer this bacterium to be more efficient in cleaning up future spills. (credit: modification of work by NOAA's National Ocean Service)

fore the invention of the microscope, the existence of many types of microbes was impossible to prove. By definition, microorganisms, or microbes, are very small organisms; many types of microbes are too small to see without a microscope, although some parasites and fungi are visible to the naked eye.

Humans have been living with—and using—microorganisms for much longer than they have been able to see them. Historical evidence suggests that humans have had some notion of microbial life since prehistoric times and have used that knowledge to develop foods as well as prevent and treat disease. In this section, we will explore some of the historical applications of microbiology as well as the early beginnings of microbiology as a science.

Instruments of Microscopy

Many types of microscopes fall under the category of **light microscopes**, which use light to visualize images. The specific type of light microscope found in most microbiology labs is the bright field microscope. The maximum theoretical resolution of images created by light microscopes is ultimately limited by the wavelengths of visible light. Most light microscopes can only magnify 1000x, and a few can magnify up to 1500x, but this does not begin to approach the magnifying power of an **electron microscope (EM)** which uses short-wavelength electron beams rather than light to increase magnification and resolution.

ELECTRON MICROSCOPES	Magnification: 20–100,000x or more	
Use electron beams focused with magnets to produce an image.		
Microscope Type	**Key Uses**	**Sample Images**
Transmission (TEM)	Uses electron beams that pass through a specimen to visualize small images; useful to observe small, thin specimens such as tissue sections and subcellular structures. **Example:** *Ebola* virus	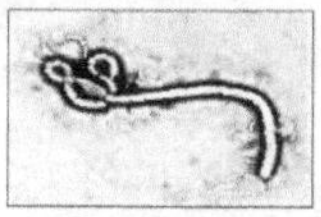
Scanning (SEM)	Uses electron beams to visualize surfaces; useful to observe the three-dimensional surface details of specimens. **Example:** *Campylobacter jejuni*	

Figure 2 *(credit "TEM": modification of work by American Society for Microbiology; credit "SEM": modification of work by American Society for Microbiology)*

There are two basic types of EM: the **transmission electron microscope (TEM)** and the **scanning electron microscope (SEM)**. Images obtained using TEM are made from very thin sections and appear two dimensional. SEM provides a more three dimensional image of the surface of cells.

Types of Microorganisms

Beyond these basic components, cells can vary greatly between organisms, and even within the same multicellular organism. The two largest categories of cells—**prokaryotic cells** and **eukaryotic cells**—are defined by major differences in several cell structures. Prokaryotic cells lack a nucleus surrounded by a complex nuclear membrane and generally have a single, circular chromosome located in a nucleoid. Eukaryotic cells have a nucleus surrounded by a complex nuclear membrane that contains multiple, rod-shaped chromosomes. In addition, some microorganisms are not made of cells and are considered **acellular**.

Prokaryotic Microorganisms

Bacteria are found in nearly every habitat on earth, including within and on humans. Most bacteria are harmless or helpful, but some are **pathogens**, causing disease in humans and other animals. Bacteria are prokaryotic because their genetic material (DNA) is not housed within a true nucleus. Most bacteria have cell walls that contain peptidoglycan.

Bacteria are often described in terms of their general shape. Common shapes include spherical (coccus), rod-shaped (bacillus), or curved (spirillum, spirochete, or vibrio).

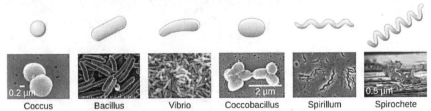

| Coccus | Bacillus | Vibrio | Coccobacillus | Spirillum | Spirochete |

Figure 4 *Common bacterial shapes. Note how coccobacillus is a combination of spherical (coccus) and rod-shaped (bacillus). (credit "Coccus": modification of work by Janice Haney Carr, Centers for Disease Control and Prevention; credit "Coccobacillus": modification of work by Janice Carr, Centers for Disease Control and Prevention; credit "Spirochete": Centers for Disease Control and Prevention)*

They have a wide range of metabolic capabilities and can grow in a variety of environments, using different combinations of nutrients. Some bacteria are photosynthetic, such as oxygenic cyanobacteria and anoxygenic green sulfur and green nonsulfur bacteria; these bacteria use energy derived from sunlight, and fix carbon dioxide for growth. Other types of bacteria are nonphotosynthetic, obtaining their energy from organic or inorganic compounds in their environment.

Archaea are also unicellular prokaryotic organisms. Archaea and bacteria have different evolutionary histories, as well as significant differences in genetics, metabolic pathways, and the composition of their cell walls and membranes. Unlike most bacteria, archaeal cell walls do not contain peptidoglycan, but their cell walls are often composed of a similar substance called pseudopeptidoglycan. Like bacteria, archaea are found in nearly every habitat on earth, even extreme environments that are very cold, very hot, very basic, or very acidic. Some archaea live in the human body, but none have been shown to be human pathogens.

Eukaryotic Microorganisms

The domain Eukarya contains all eukaryotes, including uni- or multicellular eukaryotes such as protists, fungi, plants, and animals. The major defining characteristic of eukaryotes is that their cells contain a nucleus.

Protists are an informal grouping of eukaryotes that are not plants, animals, or fungi. Algae and protozoa are examples of protists.

Algae (singular: alga) are protists that can be either unicellular or multicellular and vary widely in size, appearance, and habitat . Their cells are surrounded by cell walls made of cellulose, a type of carbohydrate. Algae are photosynthetic organisms that extract energy from the sun and release oxygen and carbohydrates into their environment. Because other organisms can use their waste products for energy, algae are important parts of many ecosystems. Many consumer products contain ingredients derived from algae, such as carrageenan or alginic acid, which are found in some brands of ice cream, salad dressing, beverages, lipstick, and toothpaste. A derivative of algae also plays a prominent role in the microbiology laboratory. Agar, a gel derived from algae, can be mixed with various nutrients and used to grow microorganisms in a Petri dish. Algae are also being developed as a possible source for biofuels.

Protozoa (singular: protozoan) are protists that make up the backbone of many food webs by providing nutrients for other organisms. Protozoa are very diverse. Some protozoa move with help from hair-like structures called cilia or whip-like structures called flagella. Others extend part of their cell membrane and cytoplasm to propel themselves forward. These cytoplasmic extensions are called pseudopods ("false feet"). Some protozoa are photosynthetic; others feed on organic material. Some are free-living, whereas others are parasitic, only able to survive by extracting nutrients from a host organism. Most protozoa are harmless, but some are pathogens that can cause disease in animals or humans.

Fungi (singular: fungus) are also eukaryotes. Some multicellular fungi, such as mushrooms, resemble plants, but they are actually quite different. Fungi are not photosynthetic, and their cell walls are usually made out of chitin rather than cellulose. Unicellular fungi, **yeasts,** are included within the study of microbiology. There are more than 1000 known species. Yeasts are found in many different environments, from the deep sea to the human navel. Some yeasts have beneficial

Figure 5 *Some archaea live in extreme environments, such as the Morning Glory pool, a hot spring in Yellowstone National Park. The color differences in the pool result from the different communities of microbes that are able to thrive at various water temperatures.*

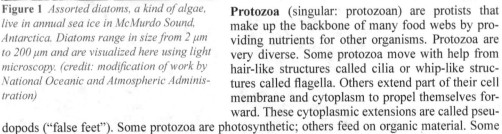

Figure 1 *Assorted diatoms, a kind of algae, live in annual sea ice in McMurdo Sound, Antarctica. Diatoms range in size from 2 μm to 200 μm and are visualized here using light microscopy. (credit: modification of work by National Oceanic and Atmospheric Administration)*

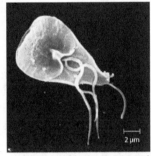

Figure 6 *Giardia lamblia, an intestinal protozoan parasite that infects humans and other mammals, causing severe diarrhea. (credit: modification of work by Centers for Disease Control and Prevention)*

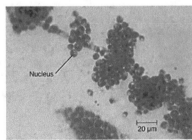

Figure 7 *Candida albicans is a unicellular fungus, or yeast. It is the causative agent of vaginal yeast infections as well as oral thrush, a yeast infection of the mouth that commonly afflicts infants. C. albicans has a morphology similar to that of coccus bacteria; however, yeast is a eukaryotic organism (note the nuclei) and is much larger. (credit: modification of work by Centers for Disease Control and Prevention)*

uses, such as causing bread to rise and beverages to ferment; but yeasts can also cause food to spoil. Some even cause diseases, such as vaginal yeast infections and oral thrush.

Other fungi of interest to microbiologists are multicellular organisms called molds. Molds are made up of long filaments that form visible colonies. Molds are found in many different environments, from soil to rotting food to dank bathroom corners. Molds play a critical role in the decomposition of dead plants and animals. Some molds can cause allergies, and others produce disease-causing metabolites called mycotoxins. Molds have been used to make pharmaceuticals, including penicillin, which is one of the most commonly prescribed antibiotics, and cyclosporine, used to prevent organ rejection following a transplant.

Figure 8 *Large colonies of microscopic fungi can often be observed with the naked eye, as seen on the surface of these moldy oranges.*

Acellular Microorganisms

Viruses are acellular microorganisms, which means they are not composed of cells. Essentially, a virus consists of proteins and genetic material—either DNA or RNA, but never both—that are inert outside of a host organism. However, by incorporating themselves into a host cell, viruses are able to co-opt the host's cellular mechanisms to multiply and infect other hosts.

Viruses can infect all types of cells, from human cells to the cells of other microorganisms. In humans, viruses are responsible for numerous diseases, from the common cold to deadly Ebola . However, many viruses do not cause disease.

Like viruses, **prions** are acellular microorganisms. But, unlike viruses, they are made ONLY of protein. They do not contain nucleic acid of any kind. Prions appear to be relatively rare and cause neurological disease in infected animals including humans. Bovine spongiform encephalopathy ("Mad cow disease") and chronic wasting disease in deer and elk are caused by prions.

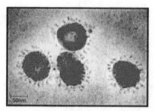
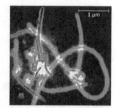
(a)   (b)

Figure 9 *(a) Members of the Coronavirus family can cause respiratory infections like the common cold, severe acute respiratory syndrome (SARS), and Middle East respiratory syndrome (MERS). Here they are viewed under a transmission electron microscope (TEM). (b) Ebolavirus, a member of the Filovirus family, as visualized using a TEM. (credit a: modification of work by Centers for Disease Control and Prevention; credit b: modification of work by Thomas W. Geisbert)*

Early History of Microbiology

Several ancient civilizations appear to have had some understanding that disease could be transmitted by things they could not see. This is especially evident in historical attempts to contain the spread of disease. For example, the Bible refers to the practice of quarantining people with leprosy and other diseases, suggesting that people understood that diseases could be communicable. Ironically, while leprosy is communicable, it is also a disease that progresses slowly. This means that people were likely quarantined after they had already spread the disease to others.

The ancient Greeks attributed disease to bad air, *mal'aria*, which they called "miasmatic odors." They developed hygiene practices that built on this idea. The Romans also believed in the miasma hypothesis and created a complex sanitation infrastructure to deal with sewage. In Rome, they built aqueducts, which brought fresh water into the city, and a giant sewer, the *Cloaca Maxima*, which carried waste away and into the river Tiber. Some researchers believe that this infrastructure helped protect the Romans from epidemics of waterborne illnesses.

vanLeeuwenhoek and the Discovery of Microorganisms

While the ancients may have suspected the existence of invisible "minute creatures," it wasn't until the invention of the microscope that their existence was definitively confirmed. While it is unclear who exactly invented the microscope, a Dutch cloth merchant named Antonie van Leeuwenhoek (1632–1723) was the first to develop a lens powerful enough to view microbes. In 1675, using a simple but powerful microscope, Leeuwenhoek was able to observe single-celled organisms, which he described as "animalcules" or "wee little beasties," swimming in a drop of rain water. From his drawings of these little organisms, we now know he was looking at bacteria and protists.

Antonie van Leeuwenhoek, sometimes hailed as "the Father of Microbiology," is typically credited as the first person to have created microscopes powerful enough to view microbes. Born in the city of Delft in the Dutch Republic, van Leeuwenhoek began his career selling fabrics. However, he later became interested in lens making (perhaps to look at threads) and his innovative techniques produced microscopes that allowed him to observe microorganisms as no one had before. In 1674, he described his observations of single-celled organisms, whose existence was previously unknown, in a series of letters to the Royal Society of London. His report was initially met with skepticism, but his claims were soon verified and

(a)   (b)   (c)

Figure 10 *(a) Antonie van Leeuwenhoek (1632–1723) is credited as being the first person to observe microbes, including bacteria, which he called "animalcules" and "wee little beasties." (b) Even though van Leeuwenhoek's microscopes were simple microscopes (as seen in this replica), they were more powerful and provided better resolution than the compound microscopes of his day. (c) Though more famous for developing the telescope, Galileo Galilei (1564–1642) was also one of the pioneers of microscopy. (credit b: modification of work by "Wellcome Images"/Wikimedia Commons)*

he became something of a celebrity in the scientific community.

The Golden Age of Microbiology

Nearly 200 years after van Leeuwenhoek got his first glimpse of microbes, the "Golden Age of Microbiology" spawned a host of new discoveries between 1857 and 1914. Two famous microbiologists, **Louis** Pasteur and **Robert** Koch, were especially active in advancing our understanding of the unseen world of microbes. Pasteur, a French chemist, showed that individual microbial strains had unique properties and demonstrated that fermentation is caused by microorganisms. He also invented pasteurization, a process used to kill microorganisms responsible for spoilage, and developed vaccines for the treatment of diseases, including rabies, in animals and humans. Koch, a German physician, was the first to demonstrate the connection between a single, isolated microbe and a known human disease. For example, he discovered the bacteria that cause anthrax (*Bacillus anthracis*), cholera (*Vibrio cholera*), and tuberculosis (*Mycobacterium tuberculosis*). We will discuss these famous microbiologists, and others, in later chapters.

(a)   (b)

Figure 11 *(a) Louis Pasteur (1822–1895) is credited with numerous innovations that advanced the fields of microbiology and immunology. (b) Robert Koch (1843–1910) identified the specific microbes that cause anthrax, cholera, and tuberculosis.*

As microbiology has developed, it has allowed the broader discipline of biology to grow and flourish in previously unimagined ways. Much of what we know about human cells comes from our understanding of microbes, and many of the tools we use today to study cells and their genetics derive from work with microbes.

Naming Microorganisms

All living organisms are assigned scientific names. Most microorganisms do not have common names like we have for trees (oak, maple) or animals (raccoon, mouse). Therefore, understanding the conventions of scientific names is important for microbiologists.

For naming living organisms, scientists use a system of **binomial nomenclature**, a two-word naming system for identifying organisms by **genus** and **specific epithet**. For example, modern humans are in the genus *Homo* and have the specific epithet name *sapiens*, so their scientific name in binomial nomenclature is *Homo sapiens*. In binomial nomenclature, the genus part of the name is always capitalized; it is followed by the specific epithet name, which is not capitalized. Both names are italicized. When referring to the **species** of humans, the binomial nomenclature would be *Homo sapiens*.

Taxonomic names in the 18th through 20th centuries were typically derived from Latin, since that was the common language used by scientists when taxonomic systems were first created. Today, newly discovered organisms can be given names derived from Latin, Greek, or English. Sometimes these names reflect some distinctive trait of the organism; in other cases, microorganisms are named after the scientists who discovered them. The archaeon *Haloquadratum walsbyi* is an example of both of these naming schemes. The genus, *Haloquadratum*, describes the microorganism's saltwater habitat (*halo* is derived from the Greek word for "salt") as well as the arrangement of its square cells, which are arranged in square clusters of four cells (*quadratum* is Latin for "foursquare"). The species, *walsbyi*, is named after Anthony Edward Walsby, the microbiologist who discovered *Haloquadratum walsbyi* in in 1980.

In this text, we will typically abbreviate an organism's genus and species after its first mention. The abbreviated form is simply the first initial of the genus, followed by a period and the full name of the species. For example, the bacterium *Escherichia coli* is shortened to *E. coli* in its abbreviated form. You will encounter this same convention in other scientific texts as well. Finally, scientific names are typically italicized (*E. coli*) when typing and underlined when hand writing (E. coli).

Bacterial Strains

Within one species of microorganism, there can be several subtypes called **strains.** While different strains may be nearly identical genetically, they can have very different attributes. The bacterium *Escherichia coli* is infamous for causing food poisoning and traveler's diarrhea. However, there are actually many different strains of *E. coli*, and they vary in their ability to cause disease.

One pathogenic (disease-causing) *E. coli* strain that you may have heard of is *E. coli* O157:H7. In humans, infection from *E. coli* O157:H7 can cause abdominal cramps and diarrhea. Infection usually originates from contaminated water or food, particularly raw vegetables and undercooked meat. In the 1990s, there were several large outbreaks of *E. coli* O157:H7 thought to have originated in undercooked hamburgers.

While *E. coli* O157:H7 and some other strains have given *E. coli* a bad name, most *E. coli* strains do not cause disease. In fact, some can be helpful. Different strains of *E. coli* found naturally in our gut help us digest our food, provide us with some needed chemicals, and fight against pathogenic microbes.

Helicobacter pylori

The gram-negative bacterium ***Helicobacter pylori*** is able to tolerate the acidic environment of the human stomach and has been shown to be a major cause of **peptic ulcers**, which are ulcers of the stomach or duodenum. The bacterium is also associated with increased risk of stomach cancer. According to the CDC, approximately two-thirds of the population is infected with *H. pylori,* but less than 20% have

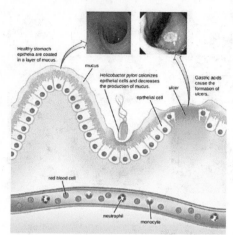

Figure 12 *Helicobacter infection decreases mucus production and causes peptic ulcers. (credit top left photo: modification of work by "Santhosh Thomas"/YouTube; credit top right photo: modification of work by Moriya M, Uehara A, Okumura T, Miyamoto M, and Kohgo Y)*

a risk of developing ulcers or stomach cancer. *H. pylori* is found in approximately 80% of stomach ulcers and in over 90% of duodenal ulcers.

Signs and symptoms include nausea, lack of appetite, bloating, burping, and weight loss. Bleeding ulcers may produce dark stools. If no treatment is provided, the ulcers can become deeper, more tissues can be involved, and stomach perforation can occur. Because perforation allows digestive enzymes and acid to leak into the body, it is a very serious condition.

To diagnose *H. pylori* infection, multiple methods are available. In a breath test, the patient swallows radiolabeled urea. If *H. pylori* is present, the bacteria will produce urease to break down the urea. This reaction produces radiolabeled carbon dioxide that can be detected in the patient's breath. Blood testing can also be used to detect antibodies to *H. pylori*. The bacteria themselves can be detected using either a stool test or a stomach wall biopsy.

Antibiotics can be used to treat the infection. However, unique to *H. pylori,* the recommendation from the US Food and Drug Administration is to use a triple therapy. Although treatment is often valuable, there are also risks to *H. pylori* eradication. Infection with *H. pylori* may actually protect against some cancers, such as esophageal adenocarcinoma and gastroesophageal reflux disease.

Symbiotic Relationships

As we have learned, prokaryotic microorganisms can associate with plants and animals. Often, this association results in unique relationships between organisms. For example, bacteria living on the roots or leaves of a plant get nutrients from the plant and, in return, produce substances that protect the plant from pathogens. On the other hand, some bacteria are plant pathogens that use mechanisms of infection similar to bacterial pathogens of animals and humans.

Any interaction between different species that are associated with each other within a community is called **symbiosis**. Such interactions fall along a continuum between opposition and cooperation. Interactions in a symbiotic relationship may be beneficial or harmful, or have no effect on one or both of the species involved.

Types of Symbiotic Relationships		
Type	**Population A**	**Population B**
Mutualism	Benefitted	Benefitted
Commensalism	Benefitted	Unaffected
Parasitism	Benefitted	Harmed

When two species benefit from each other, the symbiosis is called **mutualism**. For example, humans have a mutualistic relationship with the bacterium *Bacteroides thetaiotaomicron*, which lives in the intestinal tract. *Bacteroides thetaiotaomicron* digests complex polysaccharide plant materials that human digestive enzymes cannot break down, converting them into monosaccharides that can be absorbed by human cells. Humans also have a mutualistic relationship with certain strains of *Escherichia coli*, another bacterium found in the gut. *E. coli* relies on intestinal contents for nutrients, and humans derive certain vitamins from *E. coli,* particularly vitamin K, which is required for the formation of blood clotting factors. (This is only true for some strains of *E. coli*, however. Other strains are pathogenic and do not have a mutualistic relationship with humans.)

In another type of symbiosis, called **commensalism**, one organism benefits while the other is unaffected. This occurs when the bacterium *Staphylococcus epidermidis* uses the dead cells of the human skin as nutrients. Billions of these bacteria live on our skin, but in most cases (especially when our immune system is healthy), we do not react to them in any way. *S. epidermidis* provides an excellent example of how the classifications of symbiotic relationships are not always distinct. One could also consider the symbiotic relationship of *S. epidermidis* with humans as mutualism. Humans provide a food source of dead skin cells to the bacterium, and in turn the production of bacteriocin can provide defense against potential pathogens.

A type of symbiosis in which one organism benefits while harming the other is called **parasitism**. The relationship between humans and many pathogenic prokaryotes can be characterized as parasitic because these organisms invade the body, producing toxic substances or infectious diseases that cause harm. Diseases such as tetanus, diphtheria, pertussis, tuberculosis, and leprosy all arise from interactions between bacteria and humans.

Microbiota of the Human Body

The **normal microbiota** are all the prokaryotic and eukaryotic microorganisms that are associated with a certain organism or environment. The normal microbiota of the human may be **resident microbiota**, those organisms that constantly live in or on our bodies or **transient microbiota** those organisms that are only temporarily found in or on the human body. Hygiene and diet can alter the make-up of the normal microbiota. Despite all of the positive and helpful roles prokaryotes play, some are human **pathogens** that may cause illness or infection when they enter the body. Less than 1% of prokaryotes (all of them bacteria) are thought to be human pathogens, but collectively these species are responsible for a large number of the diseases that afflict humans.

Prokaryotes are abundant on and within the human body. According to a report by National Institutes of Health, prokaryotes, especially bacteria, outnumber human cells 10:1. More recent studies suggest the ratio could be closer to 1:1, but even that ratio means that there are a great number of bacteria within the human body. Bacteria thrive in the human mouth, nasal cavity, throat, ears, gastrointestinal tract, and vagina. Large colonies of bacteria can be found on healthy human skin, especially in moist areas (armpits, navel, and areas behind ears). However, even drier areas of the skin are not free from bacteria. The abundance of microbiota are by far the greatest in the large intestine.

The resident microbiota is amazingly diverse, not only in terms of the variety of species but also in terms of the preference of different microorganisms for different areas of the human body. For example, in the human mouth, there are thousands of commensal or mutual-istic species of bacteria. Some of these bacteria prefer to inhabit the surface of the tongue, whereas others prefer the internal surface of the cheeks, and yet others prefer the front or back teeth or gums. The inner surface of the cheek has the least diverse microbiota because of its exposure to oxygen. By contrast, the crypts of the tongue and the spaces between teeth are two sites with limited oxygen exposure, so these sites have more diverse microbiota, including bacteria living in the absence of oxygen (e.g., *Bacteroides*, *Fusobacterium*). Differences in the oral microbiota between randomly chosen human individuals are also significant. Studies have shown, for example, that the prevalence of such bacteria as *Streptococcus*, *Haemophilus*, *Neisseria*, and others was dramatically different when compared between individuals.

There are also significant differences between the microbiota of different sites of the same human body. The inner surface of the cheek has a predominance of *Streptococcus*, whereas in the throat, the palatine tonsil, and saliva, there are two to three times fewer *Streptococcus*, and several times more *Fusobacterium*. In the plaque removed from gums, the predominant bacteria belong to the genus *Fusobacterium*. However, in the intestine, both *Streptococcus* and *Fusobacterium* disappear, and the genus *Bacteroides* becomes predominant.

Not only can the microbiota vary from one body site to another, the microbiome can also change over time within the same individual. Humans acquire their first inoculations of normal flora during natural birth and shortly after birth. Before birth, there is a rapid increase in the population of **Lactobacillus** spp. in the vagina, and this population serves as the first colonization of microbiota during natural birth. After birth, additional microbes are acquired from health-care providers, parents, other relatives, and individuals who come in contact with the baby. This process establishes a microbiome that will continue to evolve over the course of the individual's life as new microbes colonize and are eliminated from the body. For example, it is estimated that within a 9-hour period, the microbiota of the small intestine can change so that half of the microbial inhabitants will be different. The importance of the initial *Lactobacillus* colonization during vaginal child birth is highlighted by studies demonstrating a higher incidence of diseases in individuals born by cesarean section, compared to those born vaginally. Studies have shown that babies born vaginally are predominantly colonized by vaginal lactobacillus, whereas babies born by cesarean section are more frequently colonized by microbes of the normal skin microbiota, including common hospital-acquired pathogens.

Throughout the body, resident microbiotas are important for human health because they occupy niches that might be otherwise taken by pathogenic microorganisms. For instance, *Lactobacillus* spp. are the dominant bacterial species of the normal vaginal microbiota for most women. *Lactobacillus* produce lactic acid, contributing to the acidity of the vagina and inhibiting the growth of pathogenic yeasts. However, when the population of the resident microbiota is decreased for some reason (e.g., because of taking antibiotics), the pH of the vagina increases, making it a more favorable environment for the growth of yeasts such as *Candida albicans*. Antibiotic therapy can also disrupt the microbiota of the intestinal tract and respiratory tract, increasing the risk for secondary infections and/or promoting the long-term carriage and shedding of pathogens.

The environment of most of the GI (gastrointestinal) tract is harsh, which serves two purposes: digestion and immunity. The stomach is an extremely acidic environment (pH 1.5–3.5) due to the gastric juices that break down food and kill many ingested microbes; this helps prevent infection from pathogens. The environment in the small intestine is less harsh and is able to support microbial communities. Compared to the small intestine, the large intestine (colon) contains a diverse and abundant microbiota that is important for normal func-tion. In addition to bacteria, methanogenic archaea and some fungi are also present. These microbes all aid in digestion and contribute to the production of feces, the waste excreted from the digestive tract, and flatus, the gas produced from microbial fermentation of undi-gested food. They can also produce valuable nutrients. For example, lactic acid bacteria such as bifidobacteria can synthesize vitamins, such as vitamin B12, folate, and riboflavin, that humans cannot synthesize themselves. *E. coli* found in the intestine can also break down food and help the body produce vitamin K, which is important for blood coagulation.

The constant movement of materials through the gastrointestinal tract also helps to move transient pathogens out of the body. In fact, feces are composed of approximately 25% microbes, 25% sloughed epithelial cells, 25% mucus, and 25% digested or undigested food. Finally, the normal microbiota provides an additional barrier to infection via a variety of mechanisms. For example, these organisms outcompete potential pathogens for space and nutrients within the intestine.

The skin is home to a wide variety of normal microbiota, consisting of commensal organisms that derive nutrition from skin cells and secretions such as sweat and sebum. The normal microbiota of skin tends to inhibit transient-microbe colonization by producing antimi-crobial substances and outcompeting other microbes that land on the surface of the skin. This helps to protect the skin from pathogenic infection.

The skin's properties differ from one region of the body to another, as does the composition of the skin's microbiota. The availability of nutrients and moisture partly dictates which microorganisms will thrive in a particular region of the skin. Relatively moist skin, such as that of the nares (nostrils) and underarms, has a much different microbiota than the dryer skin on the arms, legs, hands, and top of the feet. Some areas of the skin have higher densities of sebaceous glands. These sebum-rich areas, which include the back, the folds at the side of the nose, and the back of the neck, harbor distinct microbial communities that are less diverse than those found on other parts of the body.

Different types of bacteria dominate the dry, moist, and sebum-rich regions of the skin. The most abundant microbes typically found in the dry and sebaceous regions are Betaproteobacteria and Propionibacteria, respectively. In the moist regions, *Corynebacterium* and *Staphylococcus* are most commonly found. Viruses and fungi are also found on the skin, with *Malassezia* being the most common type of fungus found as part of the normal microbiota. The role and populations of viruses in the microbiota are still not well understood, and there are limitations to the techniques used to identify them.

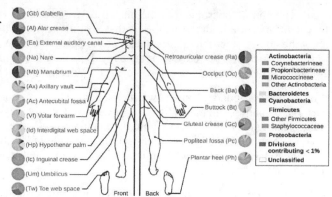

Figure 13 *The normal microbiota varies on different regions of the skin, especially in dry versus moist areas. The figure shows the major organisms commonly found in different locations of a healthy individual's skin and external mucosa. Note that there is significant variation among individuals. (credit: modification of work by National Human Genome Research Institute)*

Human Microbiome

The **human microbiome** is all the genetic material of the human normal microbiota. One of the challenges in understanding the normal microbiota has been the difficulty of culturing many of the microbes that inhabit the human body. It has been estimated that we are only able to culture 1% of the bacteria in nature and that we are unable to grow the remaining 99%. To address this challenge, researchers have used **metagenomic** analysis, which studies genetic material harvested directly from microbial communities, as opposed to that of individual species grown in a culture. This allows researchers to study the genetic material of all microbes in the microbiome, rather than just those that can be cultured

The Human Microbiome Project was launched by the National Institutes of Health (NIH) in 2008. One main goal of the project is to create a large repository of the gene sequences of important microbes found in humans, helping biologists and clinicians understand the dynamics of the human microbiome and the relationship between the human microbiota and diseases. A network of labs working together has been compiling the data from swabs of several areas of the skin, gut, and mouth from hundreds of individuals.

One important achievement of the Human Microbiome Project is establishing the first reference database on microorganisms living in and on the human body. Many of the microbes in the microbiome are beneficial, but some are not. It was found, somewhat unexpectedly, that all of us have some serious microbial pathogens in our microbiota. For example, the conjunctiva of the human eye contains 24 genera of bacteria and numerous pathogenic species. A healthy human mouth contains a number of species of the genus *Streptococcus*, including pathogenic species *S. pyogenes* and *S. pneumoniae*.This raises the question of why certain prokaryotic organisms exist commensally in certain individuals but act as deadly pathogens in others. Also unexpected was the number of organisms that had never been cultured. For example, in one metagenomic study of the human gut microbiota, 174 new species of bacteria were identified.

Prokaryotic Cells – Structure and Function

At the simplest level of construction, all cells possess a few fundamental components. These include **cytoplasm** (a gel-like substance composed of water and dissolved chemicals needed for growth), which is contained within a **plasma membrane** (also called a cell membrane or cytoplasmic membrane); one or more **chromosomes**, which contain the genetic blueprints of the cell; and **ribosomes**, organelles used for the production of proteins.

All plant cells and animal cells are eukaryotic. Some microorganisms are composed of prokaryotic cells, whereas others are composed of eukaryotic cells. Most microbes are unicellular and small enough that they require artificial magnification to be seen. However, there are some unicellular microbes that are visible to the naked eye, and some multicellular organisms that are microscopic. An object must measure about 100 micrometers (μm) to be visible without a microscope, but most microorganisms are many times smaller than that. For some perspective, consider that a typical animal cell measures roughly 10 μm across but is still microscopic. Bacterial cells are typically about 1 μm, and viruses can be 10 times smaller than bacteria. See the table below for units of length used in microbiology.

Microorganisms differ from each other not only in size, but also in structure, habitat, metabolism, and many other characteristics. While we typically think of microorganisms as being unicellular, there are also many multicellular organisms that are too small to be seen without a microscope. Some microbes, such as viruses, are even acellular (not composed of cells).

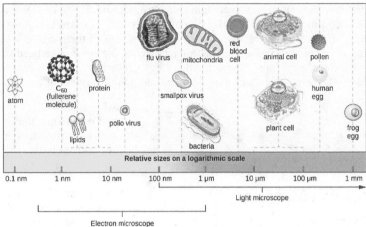

Figure 1 *The relative sizes of various microscopic and nonmicroscopic objects. Note that a typical virus measures about 100 nm, 10 times smaller than a typical bacterium (~1 μm), which is at least 10 times smaller than a typical plant or animal cell (~10–100 μm). An object must measure about 100 μm to be visible without a microscope.*

Common Cell Morphologies and Arrangements

Individual cells of a particular prokaryotic organism are typically similar in shape, or **cell morphology**. Although thousands of prokaryotic organisms have been identified, only a handful of cell morphologies are commonly seen microscopically. The three main cell shapes are coccus (round), bacillus (rod shaped) and spirals (curved or spiral). In addition to cellular shape, prokaryotic cells of the same species may group together in certain distinctive **arrangements** depending on the plane of cell division. Some of the common arrangements include **diplococcus** (pairs or round cells), **tetrads** (four round cells), **streptococcus** (chains of round cells), **staphylococcus** (clusters of round cells), and **streptobacillus** (chains of rod shaped cells).

Common Prokaryotic Cell Arrangements		
Name	**Description**	**Illustration**
Coccus (pl. cocci)	Single coccus	
Diplococcus (pl. diplococci)	Pair of two cocci	
Tetrad (pl. tetrads)	Grouping of four cells arranged in a square	
Streptococcus (pl. streptococci)	Chain of cocci	
Staphylococcus (pl. staphylococci)	Cluster of cocci	
Bacillus (pl. bacilli)	Single rod	
Streptobacillus (pl. streptobacilli)	Chain of rods	

Common Prokaryotic Cell Shapes			
Name	**Description**	**Illustration**	**Image**
Coccus (pl. cocci)	Round		
Bacillus (pl. bacilli)	Rod		
Vibrio (pl. vibrios)	Curved rod		
Coccobacillus (pl. coccobacilli)	Short rod		
Spirillum (pl. spirilla)	Spiral		
Spirochete (pl. spirochetes)	Long, loose, helical spiral		

Structures Inside Prokaryotic Cells

All cellular life has a DNA genome organized into one or more **chromosomes**. Prokaryotic chromosomes are typically circular, haploid (unpaired), and not bound by a complex nuclear membrane. Prokaryotic DNA and DNA-associated proteins are concentrated within the **nucleoid region** of the cell.

Prokaryotic cells may also contain extrachromosomal DNA, or DNA that is not part of the chromosome called **plasmids**. Plasmids are small, circular, double-stranded DNA molecules. Cells that have plasmids often have hundreds of them within a single cell. Plasmids are more commonly found in bacteria; however, plasmids have been found in archaea and eukaryotic organisms. Plasmids often carry genes that confer advantageous traits such as antibiotic resistance; thus, they are important to the survival of the organism.

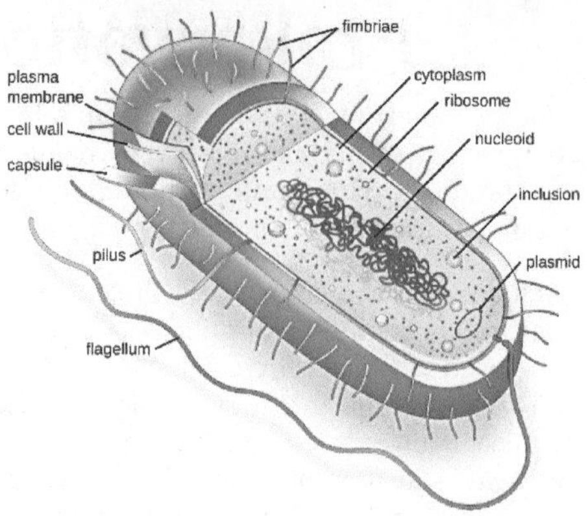

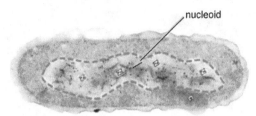

All cellular life synthesizes proteins, and organisms in all possess **ribosomes**, structures responsible for protein synthesis. Although they are the same size, bacterial and archaeal ribosomes have different proteins and rRNA molecules, and the archaeal versions are more similar to their eukaryotic counterparts than to those found in bacteria. Prokaryotic ribosomes are smaller than those of eukaryotes.

Figure 2 *A typical prokaryotic cell contains a cell membrane, chromosomal DNA that is concentrated in a nucleoid, ribosomes, and a cell wall. Some prokaryotic cells may also possess flagella, pili, fimbriae, and capsules*

Figure 3 *The nucleoid region (the area enclosed by the green dashed line) is a condensed area of DNA found within prokaryotic cells. Because of the density of the area, it does not readily stain and appears lighter in color when viewed with a transmission electron microscope.*

As single-celled organisms living in unstable environments, some prokaryotic cells have the ability to store excess nutrients within cytoplasmic structures called **inclusions**. Storing nutrients in a polymerized form is advantageous because it reduces the buildup of osmotic pressure that occurs as a cell accumulates solutes. Various types of inclusions store glycogen and starches, which contain carbon that cells can access for energy.

Some prokaryotic cells have other types of inclusions that serve purposes other than nutrient storage. For example, some prokaryotic cells produce gas vacuoles, accumulations of small, protein-lined vesicles of gas. These gas vacuoles allow the prokaryotic cells that synthesize them to alter their buoyancy so that they can adjust their location in the water column. Magnetotactic bacteria, such as *Magnetospirillum magnetotacticum*, contain magnetosomes, which are inclusions of magnetic iron oxide or iron sulfide surrounded by a lipid layer. These allow cells to align along a magnetic field, aiding their movement.

Endospores

Bacterial cells are generally observed as **vegetative cells** (metabolically active cells), but some genera of bacteria have the ability to form **endospores**, structures that essentially protect the bacterial genome in a dormant state when environmental conditions are unfavorable. Endospores (not to be confused with the reproductive spores formed by fungi) allow some bacterial cells to survive long periods without food or water, as well as exposure to chemicals, extreme temperatures, and even radiation. The process by which vegetative cells transform into endospores is called **sporulation**, and it generally begins when nutrients become depleted or environmental conditions become otherwise unfavorable.

Endospores of certain species have been shown to persist in a dormant state for extended periods of time, up to thousands of years. However, when living conditions improve, endospores undergo germination, reentering a vegetative state. After **germination**, the cell becomes metabolically active again and is able to carry out all of its normal functions, including growth and cell division.

Not all bacteria have the ability to form endospores; however, there are a number of clinically significant endospore-forming gram-positive bacteria of the genera **Bacillus** and **Clostridium**. These include *B. anthracis*, the causative agent of anthrax, which produces endospores capable of survive for many decades; *C. tetani* (causes tetanus); *C. difficile* (causes pseudomembranous colitis); *C. perfringens* (causes gas gangrene); and *C. botulinum* (causes botulism). Pathogens such as these are particularly difficult to combat because their endospores are so hard to kill.

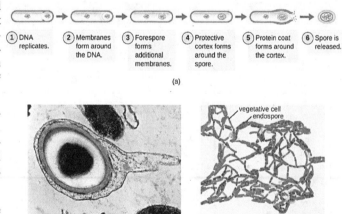

Figure 4 *(a) Sporulation begins following asymmetric cell division. The forespore becomes surrounded by a double layer of membrane, a cortex, and a protein spore coat, before being released as a mature endospore upon disintegration of the mother cell. (b) An electron micrograph of a Carboxydothermus hydrogenoformans endospore. (c) These Bacillus spp. cells are undergoing sporulation. The endospores have been visualized using Malachite Green spore stain. (credit b: modification of work by Jonathan Eisen*

Gram staining alone cannot be used to visualize endospores, which appear clear when Gram-stained cells are viewed. In the endospore stain, endospores will stain green and vegetative cells will stain red or pink. The green endospores will appear either within the pink

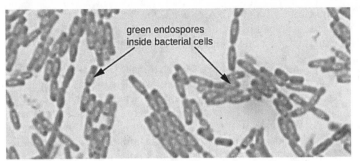

green endospores inside bacterial cells

vegetative cells or as separate from the pink cells altogether. If no endospores are present, then only the pink vegetative cells will be visible.

Endospore-staining techniques are important for identifying *Bacillus* and *Clostridium*, two genera of endospore-producing bacteria that contain clinically significant species. Among others, *B. anthracis* (which causes anthrax) has been of particular interest because of concern that its spores could be used as a bioterrorism agent. *C. difficile* is a particularly important species responsible for the typically hospital-acquired infection known as "C. diff."

Figure 5 *A stained preparation of Bacillus subtilis showing endospores as green and the vegetative cells as pink. (credit: modification of work by American Society for Microbiology)*

Plasma Membrane

Structures that enclose the cytoplasm and internal structures of the cell are known collectively as the cell envelope. In prokaryotic cells, the structures of the cell envelope vary depending on the type of cell and organism. Most (but not all) prokaryotic cells have a cell wall, but the makeup of this cell wall varies. All cells (prokaryotic and eukaryotic) have a **plasma membrane** (also called cytoplasmic membrane or cell membrane) that exhibits selective permeability, allowing some molecules to enter or leave the cell while restricting the passage of others.

The structure of the **plasma membrane** is often described in terms of the fluid mosaic model, which refers to the ability of membrane components to move fluidly within the plane of the membrane, as well as the mosaic-like composition of the components, which include a diverse array of lipid and protein components. The plasma membrane structure of most bacterial and eukaryotic cell types is a bilayer composed mainly of phospholipids formed with ester linkages and proteins. These phospholipids and proteins have the ability to move laterally within the plane of the membranes as well as between the two phospholipid layers.

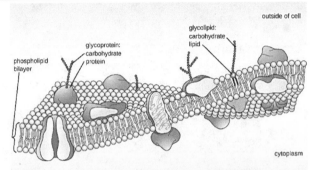

Figure 6 *The bacterial plasma membrane is a phospholipid bilayer with a variety of embedded proteins that perform various functions for the cell. Note the presence of glycoproteins and glycolipids, whose carbohydrate components extend out from the surface of the cell. The abundance and arrangement of these proteins and lipids can vary greatly between species*

Bacterial Cell Walls

Scientist **Alexander Fleming** (1881–1955) made his own accidental discovery that turned out to be monumental. In 1928, Fleming returned from holiday and examined some old plates of staphylococci in his research laboratory at St. Mary's Hospital in London. He observed that contaminating mold growth (subsequently identified as a strain of *Penicillium notatum*) inhibited staphylococcal growth on one plate. Fleming, therefore, is credited with the discovery of **penicillin**, the first **natural antibiotic**. Further experimentation showed that penicillin from the mold was antibacterial against streptococci, meningococci, and *Corynebacterium diphtheriae*, the causative agent of diphtheria.

(a)   (b)

Figure 7 *(a) Alexander Fleming was the first to discover a naturally produced antimicrobial, penicillin, in 1928. (b) Howard Florey and Ernst Chain discovered how to scale up penicillin production. Then they figured out how to purify it and showed its efficacy as an antimicrobial in animal and human trials in the early 1940s*

Fleming and his colleagues were credited with discovering and identifying penicillin, but its isolation and mass production were accomplished by a team of researchers at Oxford University under the direction of Howard Florey (1898–1968) and Ernst Chain (1906–1979). In 1940, the research team purified penicillin and reported its success as an antimicrobial agent against streptococcal infections in mice. Their subsequent work with human subjects also showed penicillin to be very effective. Because of their important work, Fleming, Florey, and Chain were awarded the Nobel Prize in Physiology and Medicine in 1945.

The primary function of the cell wall is to protect the cell from harsh conditions in the outside environment. When present, there are notable similarities and differences among the cell walls of archaea, bacteria, and eukaryotes. The major component of bacterial cell walls is called **peptidoglycan**; it is only found in bacteria. Structurally, peptidoglycan resembles a layer of meshwork or fabric. Each layer is composed of long chains of alternating molecules of carbohydrates.

Since peptidoglycan is unique to bacteria, many antibiotic drugs are designed to interfere with peptidoglycan synthesis, weakening the cell wall and making bacterial cells more susceptible to the effects of osmotic pressure. Penicillin was the first of these drugs. In addition, certain cells of the human immune system are able "recognize" bacterial pathogens by detecting peptidoglycan on the surface of a bacterial cell; these cells then engulf and destroy the bacterial cell, using enzymes such as lysozyme, which breaks down and digests the peptidoglycan in their cell walls.

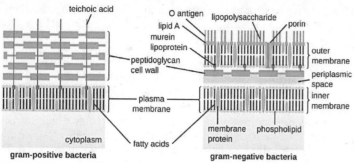

Figure 8 *Bacteria contain two common cell wall structural types. Gram-positive cell walls are structurally simple, containing a thick layer of peptidoglycan with embedded teichoic acid external to the plasma membrane.[20] Gram-negative cell walls are structurally more complex, containing three layers: the inner membrane, a thin layer of peptidoglycan, and an outer membrane containing lipopolysaccharide. (credit: modification of work by "Franciscosp2"/Wikimedia Commons)*

The Gram staining protocol is used to differentiate two common types of cell wall structures. **Gram-positive cells** have a cell wall consisting of a thick layer of peptidoglycan.

Gram-negative cells have a much thinner layer of peptidoglycan than gram-positive cells, and the overall structure of their cell envelope is more complex. There is a second lipid bilayer called the outer membrane, which is external to the peptidoglycan layer. The outer portion of the outer membrane contains the molecule **lipopolysaccharide (LPS)** containing a molecule called **Lipid A,** which functions as an endotoxin in infections involving gram-negative bacteria, contributing to symptoms such as fever, hemorrhaging, and septic shock.

Archaeal cell wall structure differs from that of bacteria in several significant ways. Most notably, archaeal cell walls do not contain peptidoglycan. As is the case with some bacterial species, there are a few archaea that appear to lack cell walls entirely.

Gram Staining

The **Gram stain** procedure is a differential staining procedure that involves multiple steps. It was developed by Danish microbiologist Hans Christian Gram in 1884 as an effective method to distinguish between bacteria with different types of cell walls, and even today it remains one of the most frequently used staining techniques. The steps of the Gram stain procedure are described in the table.

Gram stain process			
Gram staining steps	**Cell effects**	**Gram-positive**	**Gram-negative**
Step 1 **Crystal violet** *primary stain added to specimen smear.*	Stains cells purple or blue.		
Step 2 **Iodine** *mordant makes dye less soluble so it adheres to cell walls.*	Cells remain purple or blue.		
Step 3 **Alcohol** *decolorizer washes away stain from gram-negative cell walls.*	Gram-positive cells remain purple or blue. Gram-negative cells are colorless.		
Step 4 **Safranin** *counterstain allows dye adherance to gram-negative cells.*	Gram-positive cells remain purple or blue. Gram-negative cells appear pink or red.		

Figure 9 *Gram-staining is a differential staining technique that uses a primary stain and a secondary counterstain to distinguish between gram-positive and gram-negative bacteria.*

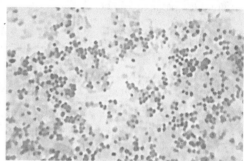

Figure 10 *In this specimen, the gram-positive bacterium Staphylococcus aureus retains crystal violet dye even after the decolorizing agent is added. Gram-negative Escherichia coli, the most common Gram stain quality-control bacterium, is decolorized, and is only visible after the addition of the pink counterstain safranin. (credit: modification of work by Nina Parker)*

The purple, crystal-violet stained cells are referred to as gram-positive cells, while the red, safranin-dyed cells are gram-negative. However, there are several important considerations in interpreting the results of a Gram stain. First, older bacterial cells may have damage to their cell walls that causes them to appear gram-negative even if the species is gram-positive. Thus, it is best to use fresh bacterial cultures for Gram staining. Second, errors such as leaving on decolorizer too long can affect the results. In some cases, most cells will appear gram-positive while a few appear gram-negative. This suggests damage to the individual cells or that decolorizer was left on for too long; the cells should still be classified as gram-positive if they are all the same species rather than a mixed culture.

Besides their differing interactions with dyes and decolorizing agents, the chemical differences between gram-positive and gram-negative cells have other implications with clinical relevance. For example, Gram staining can help clinicians classify bacterial pathogens in a sample into categories associated with specific properties. Gram-negative bacteria tend to be more resistant to certain antibiotics than gram-positive bacteria..

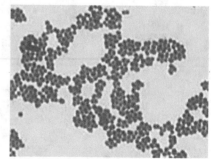

Figure 11 Gram positive staphylococci *(credit: modification of work by American Society for Microbiology)*

Bacteria that cannot be stained by the standard Gram stain procedure are called atypical bacteria. Included in the atypical category are species of *Mycoplasma* and *Chlamydia*. *Rickettsia* are also considered atypical because they are too small to be evaluated by the Gram stain.

Acid-Fast Stains

Acid-fast staining is another commonly used, differential staining technique that can be an important diagnostic tool. An acid-fast stain is able to differentiate two types of gram-positive cells: those that have waxy mycolic acids in their cell walls, and those that do not. Using the Acid-fast technique, acid-fast cells will stain red. This stain is most commonly used to identify *Mycobacterium* species such as *Mycobacterium tuberculosis* that causes tuberculosis.

Glycocalyces

Although most prokaryotic cells have cell walls, some may have additional cell envelope structures exterior to the cell wall, such as glycocalyces . A **glycocalyx** is a sugar coat, of which there are two important types: **capsules** and **slime layers** (also called extracellular polymeric substance EPS). A capsule is an organized layer located outside of the cell wall and usually composed of polysaccharides or proteins. A slime layer is a less tightly organized layer that is only loosely attached to the cell wall and can be more easily washed off. Slime layers may be composed of polysaccharides, glycoproteins, or glycolipids.

Since the presence of a capsule is directly related to a microbe's virulence (its ability to cause disease), the ability to determine whether cells in a sample have capsules is an important diagnostic tool. Capsules do not absorb most basic dyes; therefore, a negative staining technique (staining around the cells) is typically used for capsule staining. The dye stains the background but does not penetrate the capsules, which appear like halos around the borders of the cell. The specimen does not need to be heat-fixed prior to negative staining.

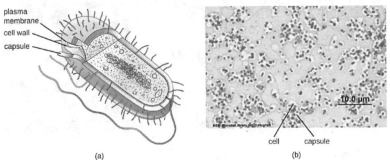

Glycocalyces allows cells to adhere to surfaces, aiding in the formation of **biofilms** (colonies of microbes that form in layers on surfaces). In nature, most microbes live in mixed communities within biofilms, partly because the biofilm affords them some level of protection. Biofilms generally hold water like a sponge, preventing desiccation. They also protect cells from predation and hinder the action of antibiotics and disinfectants. All of these properties are advantageous to the microbes living in a biofilm, but they present challenges in a clinical setting, where the goal is often to eliminate microbes.

Figure 12 *(a) Capsules are a type of glycocalyx composed of an organized layer of polysaccharides. (b) A capsule stain of Pseudomonas aeruginosa, a bacterial pathogen capable of causing many different types of infections in humans. (credit b: modification of work by American Society for Microbiology)*

The ability to produce a capsule can contribute to a microbe's pathogenicity (ability to cause disease) because the capsule can make it more difficult for phagocytic cells (such as white blood cells) to engulf and kill the microorganism. *Streptococcus pneumoniae*, for example, produces a capsule that is well known to aid in this bacterium's pathogenicity. Capsules are difficult to stain for microscopy; negative staining techniques are typically used.

Flagella

Flagella are structures used by cells to move in aqueous environments. Bacterial flagella act like propellers. Bacteria that have flagella typically can move and are considered **motile**. Those without flagella cannot move on their own and are **nonmotile**. When looking at bacteria under the microscope, even those that are nonmotile may appear to be vibrating, but not actually moving in a distinct direction. This is not motility. It is a result of collisions from molecules in the surrounding solution and is called **Brownian** movement.

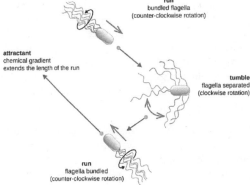

Motile bacteria can move in response to a variety of environmental signals, including light (**phototaxis**), magnetic fields (**magnetotaxis**) using magnetosomes, and, most commonly, chemical gradients (**chemotaxis**). Purposeful movement toward a chemical attractant, like a food source, or away from a repellent, like a poisonous chemical, is achieved by increasing the length of **runs** and decreasing the length of **tumbles**.

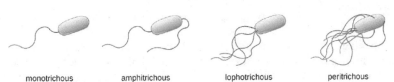

Figure 13 *Flagellated bacteria may exhibit multiple arrangements of their flagella*

Figure 14 *Without a chemical gradient, flagellar rotation cycles between counterclockwise (run) and clockwise (tumble) with no overall directional movement. However, when a chemical gradient of an attractant exists, the length of runs is extended, while the length of tumbles is decreased. This leads to chemotaxis: an overall directional movement toward the higher concentration of the attractant.*

The Eukaryotic Microorganisms

Eukaryotic organisms include protozoans, algae, fungi, plants, and animals. Some eukaryotic cells are independent, single-celled microorganisms, whereas others are part of multicellular organisms. The cells of eukaryotic organisms have several distinguishing characteristics. Above all, eukaryotic cells are defined by the presence of a nucleus surrounded by a complex nuclear membrane. Also, eukaryotic cells are characterized by the presence of membrane-bound organelles in the cytoplasm. Organelles such as mitochondria, the endoplasmic reticulum (ER), Golgi apparatus, lysosomes, and peroxisomes are held in place by the cytoskeleton, an internal network that supports transport of intracellular components and helps maintain cell shape. The genome of eukaryotic cells is packaged in multiple, rod-shaped chromosomes as opposed to the single, circular-shaped chromosome that characterizes most prokaryotic cells.

Eukaryotic microbes are an extraordinarily diverse group, including species with a wide range of life cycles, morphological specializations, and nutritional needs. Although more diseases are caused by viruses and bacteria than by microscopic eukaryotes, these eukaryotes are responsible for some diseases of great public health importance.

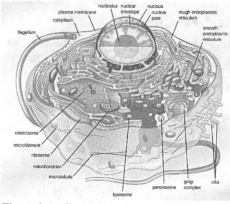

Figure 1 *An illustration of a generalized, single-celled eukaryotic organism. Note that cells of eukaryotic organisms vary greatly in terms of structure and function, and a particular cell may not have all of the structures shown here.*

Protozoans

The word *protist* is a historical term that is now used informally to refer to a diverse group of microscopic eukaryotic organisms. It is not considered a formal taxonomic term because the organisms it describes do not have a shared evolutionary origin. Historically, the protists were informally grouped into the "animal-like" protozoans, the "plant-like" algae (or microalgae), and the "fungus-like" protists such as water molds. These three groups of protists differ greatly in terms of their basic characteristics. For example, algae are photosynthetic organisms that can be unicellular or multicellular. Protozoa, on the other hand, are nonphotosynthetic, motile organisms that are always unicellular. Other informal terms may also be used to describe various groups of protists. For example, microorganisms that drift or float in water, moved by currents, are referred to as **plankton**. Protozoans inhabit a wide variety of habitats, both aquatic and terrestrial. Many are free-living, while others are parasitic, carrying out a life cycle within a host or hosts and potentially causing illness. There are also beneficial symbionts that provide metabolic services to their hosts. During the feeding and growth part of their life cycle, they are called **trophozoites;** these feed on small particulate food sources such as bacteria. While some

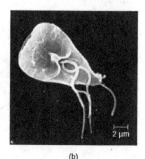

Figure 2 *(a) A scanning electron micrograph shows many Giardia parasites in the trophozoite, or feeding stage, in a gerbil intestine. (b) An individual trophozoite of G. lamblia, visualized here in a scanning electron micrograph. This waterborne protist causes severe diarrhea when ingested. (credit a, b: modification of work by Centers for Disease Control and Prevention)*

types of protozoa exist exclusively in the trophozoite form, others can develop from trophozoite to an encapsulated cyst stage when environmental conditions are too harsh for the trophozoite. A **cyst** is a cell with a protective wall, and the process by which a trophozoite becomes a cyst is called **encystment**. When conditions become more favorable, these cysts are triggered by environmental cues to become active again through excystment.

Many protozoans have whip-like flagella or hair-like cilia made of microtubules that can be used for locomotion. Others use cytoplasmic extensions known as pseudopodia ("false feet") to attach the cell to a surface; they then allow cytoplasm to flow into the extension, thus moving themselves forward. Protozoans have a variety of unique organelles and sometimes lack organelles found in other cells. Some have contractile vacuoles, organelles that can be used to move water out of the cell for osmotic regulation (salt and water balance). Mitochondria may be absent in parasites or altered.

The protists lack a shared evolutionary origin. Since the current taxonomy is based on evolutionary history (as determined by biochemistry, morphology, and genetics), protists are scattered across many different taxonomic groups within the domain Eukarya.

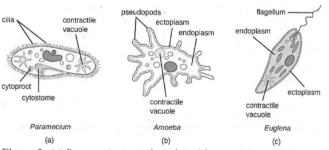

Figure 3 *(a) Paramecium spp. have hair-like appendages called cilia for locomotion. (b) Amoeba spp. use lobe-like pseudopodia to anchor the cell to a solid surface and pull forward. (c) Euglena spp. use a whip-like structure called a flagellum to propel the cell.*

One example of a disease caused by a parasitic protozoan is **malaria**, which is caused by *Plasmodium*, a eukaryotic organism transmitted through mosquito bites. Malaria is a major cause of morbidity (illness) and mortality (death) that threatens 3.4 billion people worldwide. In severe cases, organ failure and blood or metabolic abnormalities contribute to medical emergencies and sometimes death. Even after initial recovery, relapses may occur years later. In countries where malaria is endemic, the disease represents a major public health challenge that can place a tremendous strain on developing economies.

Worldwide, major efforts are underway to reduce malaria infections. Efforts include the distribution of insecticide-treated bed nets and the spraying of pesticides. Researchers are also making progress in their efforts to develop effective vaccines.[2] The President's Malaria Initiative, started in 2005, supports prevention and treatment. The Bill and Melinda Gates Foundation has a large initiative to eliminate malaria. Despite these efforts, malaria continues to cause long-term morbidity (such as intellectual disabilities in children) and mortality (especially in children younger than 5 years), so we still have far to go.

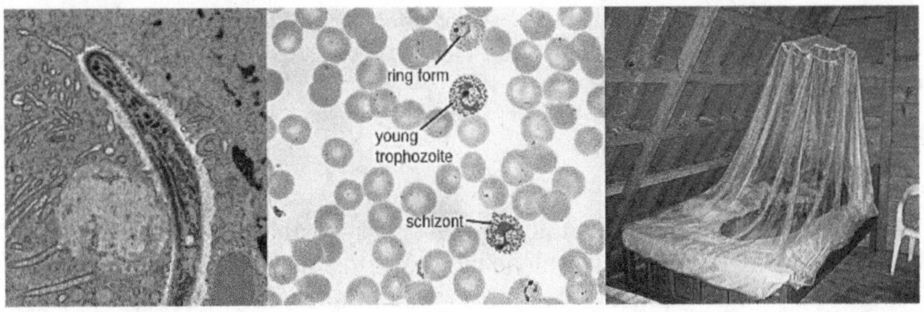

Only one major protozoan species causes infections in the urogenital system. **Trichomoniasis**, or "trich," is the most common nonviral STI and is caused by a flagellated protozoan *Trichomonas vaginalis*. *T. vaginalis* has an undulating membrane and, generally, an amoeboid shape when attached to cells in the vagina. In culture, it has an oval shape.

Figure 4 *Malaria is a disease caused by a eukaryotic parasite transmitted to humans by mosquitos. Micrographs (left and center) show a sporozoite life stage, trophozoites, and a schizont in a blood smear. On the right is depicted a primary defense against mosquito-borne illnesses like malaria—mosquito netting. (credit left: modification of work by Ute Frevert; credit middle: modification of work by Centers for Disease Control and Prevention; credit right: modification of work by Tjeerd Wiersma)*

T. vaginalis is commonly found in the normal microbiota of the vagina. As with other vaginal pathogens, it can cause vaginitis when there is disruption to the normal microbiota. It is found only as a trophozoite and does not form cysts. *T. vaginalis* is capable of phagocytosing other microbes of the normal microbiota, contributing to the development of an imbalance that is favorable to infection.

Both men and women can develop trichomoniasis. Men are generally asymptomatic, and although women are more likely to develop symptoms, they are often asymptomatic as well. When symptoms do occur, they are characteristic of urethritis. Men experience itching, irritation, discharge from the penis, and burning after urination or ejaculation. Women experience dysuria; itching, burning, redness, and soreness of the genitalia; and vaginal discharge. The infection may also spread to the cervix. Infection increases the risk of transmitting or acquiring HIV and is associated with pregnancy complications such as preterm birth. The infection is relatively easy to treat with the proper antibiotics.

Toxoplasmosis

The disease **toxoplasmosis** is caused by the protozoan *Toxoplasma gondii*. *T. gondii* is found in a wide variety of birds and mammals, and human infections are common. The Centers for Disease Control and Prevention (CDC) estimates that 22.5% of the population 12 years and older has been infected with *T. gondii*; but immunocompetent individuals are typically asymptomatic, however. Domestic cats are the only known definitive hosts for the sexual stages of *T. gondii* and, thus, are the main reservoirs of infection. Infected cats shed *T. gondii* oocysts in their feces, and these oocysts typically spread to humans through contact with fecal matter on cats' bodies, in litter boxes, or in garden beds where outdoor cats defecate.

T. gondii has a complex life cycle that involves multiple hosts. Cats may become infected after consuming birds and rodents harboring tissue cysts. Cats and other animals may also become infected directly by ingestion of sporulated oocysts in the environment. Interestingly, *Toxoplasma* infection appears to be able to modify the host's behavior. Mice infected by *Toxoplasma* lose their fear of cat pheromones. As a result, they become easier prey for cats, facilitating the transmission of the parasite to the cat.

Toxoplasma infections in humans are extremely common, but most infected people are asymptomatic or have subclinical symptoms. Some studies suggest that the parasite may be able to influence the personality and psychomotor performance of infected humans, similar to the way it modifies behavior in other mammals. When symptoms do occur, they tend to be mild and similar to those of mononucleosis. However, asymptomatic toxoplasmosis can become problematic in certain situations. Cysts can lodge in a variety of human tissues and lie dormant for years. Reactivation of these quiescent infections can occur in immunocompromised patients following transplantation, cancer therapy, or the development of an immune disorder such as AIDS. In patients with AIDS who have toxoplasmosis, the immune system cannot combat the growth of *T. gondii* in body tissues; as a result, these cysts can cause encephalitis, retinitis, pneumonitis, cognitive disorders, and seizures that can eventually be fatal.

Toxoplasmosis can also pose a risk during pregnancy because tachyzoites can cross the placenta and cause serious infections in the developing fetus. The extent of fetal damage resulting from toxoplasmosis depends on the severity of maternal disease, the damage to the placenta, the gestational age of the fetus when infected, and the virulence of the organism. Congenital toxoplasmosis often leads to fetal loss or premature birth and can result in damage to the central nervous system, manifesting as mental retardation, deafness, or blindness. Consequently, pregnant women are advised by the CDC to take particular care in preparing meat, gardening, and caring for pet cats. Diagnosis of toxoplasmosis infection during pregnancy is usually achieved by serology

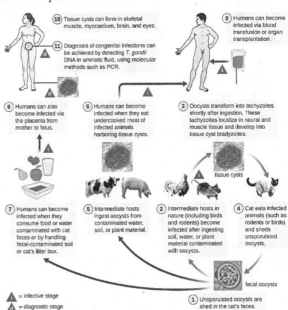

Figure 5 *The infectious cycle of Toxoplasma gondii. (credit: "diagram": modification of work by Centers for Disease Control and Prevention; credit "cat": modification of work by "KaCey97078"/Flickr)*

Preventing infection is the best first-line defense against toxoplasmosis. Preventive measures include washing hands thoroughly after handling raw meat, soil, or cat litter, and avoiding consumption of vegetables possibly contaminated with cat feces. All meat should be cooked to an internal temperature of 73.9–76.7 °C (165–170 °F).

Microalgae

The **algae** are autotrophic (photosynthetic) protists that can be unicellular or multicellular. The unicellular algae are called **microalgae**. There are many types of microalgae including the diatoms that have a silica shell on the outside. When populations of certain microalgae become particularly dense, a **red tide** (a type of **harmful algal bloom**) can occur. Red tides cause harm to marine life and to humans who consume contaminated marine life. Major toxin producers include *Gonyaulax* and *Alexandrium,* both of which cause paralytic shellfish poisoning. Another species, *Pfiesteria piscicida*, is known as a fish killer because, at certain parts of its life cycle, it can produce toxins harmful to fish and it appears to be responsible for a suite of symptoms, including memory loss and confusion, in humans exposed to water containing the species.

Fungi

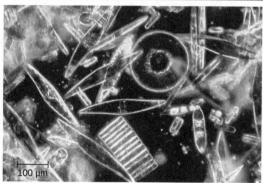

Figure 6 *Assorted diatoms, a kind of algae, live in annual sea ice in McMurdo Sound, Antarctica. Diatoms range in size from 2 µm to 200 µm and are visualized here using light microscopy. (credit: modification of work by National Oceanic and Atmospheric Administration)*

The fungi comprise a diverse group of organisms that are **heterotrophic** (use organic compounds for food) and typically **saprozoic** (feed on dead or decaying matter). In addition to the well-known macroscopic fungi (such as **mushrooms** and **molds**), many unicellular **yeasts** and spores of macroscopic fungi are microscopic. For this reason, fungi are included within the field of microbiology.

Fungi have well-defined characteristics that set them apart from other organisms. Most multicellular fungal bodies, commonly called molds, are made up of filaments called **hyphae**. Hyphae can form a tangled network called a **mycelium** and form the **thallus** (body) of fleshy fungi. There are notable unique features in fungal cell walls and membranes. In contrast to molds, yeasts are unicellular fungi. The budding yeasts reproduce asexually by budding off a smaller daughter cell; the resulting cells may sometimes stick together as a short chain or pseudohypha.

Fungal cell walls contain **chitin**, as opposed to the cellulose found in the cell walls of plants and many protists. Additionally, whereas animals have cholesterol in their cell membranes, fungal cell membranes have different sterols called ergosterols. Ergosterols are often exploited as targets for antifungal drugs.

Fungal life cycles are unique and complex. Fungi reproduce sexually either through cross- or self-fertilization. Fungi may also exhibit asexual reproduction by mitosis, mitosis with budding, fragmentation of hyphae, and formation of asexual **spores** by mitosis. These spores are specialized cells that, depending on the organism, may have unique characteristics for survival, reproduction, and dispersal. Fungi exhibit several types of asexual spores and these can be important in classification.

Some fungi are **dimorphic**, having more than one appearance during their life cycle. These dimorphic fungi may be able to appear as yeasts or molds, which can be important for infectivity. They are capable of changing their appearance in response to environmental changes such as nutrient availability or fluctuations in temperature, growing as a mold, for example, at 25 °C (77 °F), and as yeast cells at 37 °C (98.6 °F). This ability helps dimorphic fungi to survive in diverse environments. Two examples of dimorphic yeasts are the human pathogens *Histoplasma capsulatum* and *Candida albicans*. *H. capsulatum* causes the lung disease histoplasmosis, and *C. albicans* is associated with vaginal yeast infections, oral thrush, and candidiasis of the skin.

Fungi are important to humans in a variety of ways. Both microscopic and macroscopic fungi have medical relevance, with some pathogenic species that can cause **mycoses** (illnesses caused by fungi). Some pathogenic fungi are **opportunistic,** meaning that they mainly cause infections when the host's immune defenses are compromised and do not normally cause illness in healthy individuals. Fungi are important in other ways. They act as decomposers in the environment, and they are critical for the production of certain foods such as cheeses. Fungi are also major sources of antibiotics, such as penicillin from the fungus *Penicillium*.

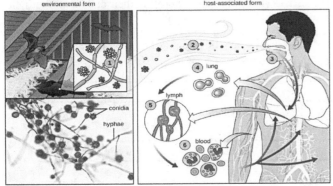

Figure 7 *Histoplasma capsulatum is a dimorphic fungus that grows in soil exposed to bird feces or bat feces (guano) (top left). It can change forms to survive at different temperatures. In the outdoors, it typically grows as a mycelium (as shown in the micrograph, bottom left), but when the spores are inhaled (right), it responds to the high internal temperature of the body (37 °C [98.6 °F]) by turning into a yeast that can multiply in the lungs, causing the chronic lung disease histoplasmosis. (credit: modification of work by Centers for Disease Control and Prevention)*

Mycoses of the Skin

Many fungal infections of the skin involve fungi that are found in the normal skin microbiota. Some of these fungi can cause infection when they gain entry through a wound; others mainly cause opportunistic infections in immunocompromised patients. Other fungal pathogens primarily cause infection in unusually moist environments that promote fungal growth; for example, sweaty shoes, communal showers, and locker rooms provide excellent breeding grounds that promote the growth and transmission of fungal pathogens.

Fungal infections, also called mycoses, can be divided into classes based on their invasiveness. Mycoses that cause superficial infections of the epidermis, hair, and nails, are called cutaneous mycoses. Mycoses that penetrate the epidermis and the dermis to infect deeper tissues are called subcutaneous mycoses. Mycoses that spread throughout the body are called systemic mycoses.

Tineas

A group of cutaneous mycoses called tineas are caused by dermatophytes, fungal molds that require **keratin**, a protein found in skin, hair, and nails, for growth. Tineas on most areas of the body are generally called ringworm, but tineas in specific locations may have distinctive names and symptoms. Keep in mind that these names—even though they are Latinized—refer to locations on the body, not causative organisms. Tineas can be caused by different dermatophytes in most areas of the body.

Some Common Tineas and Location on the Body	
Tinea corporis (ringworm)	Body
Tinea capitis (ringworm)	Scalp
Tinea pedis (athlete's foot)	Feet
Tinea barbae (barber's itch)	Beard
Tinea cruris (jock itch)	Groin
Tinea unguium (onychomycosis)	Toenails, fingernails

Table 1

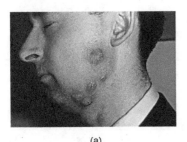
(a)

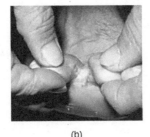
(b)

(c)

Figure 8 *Tineas are superficial cutaneous mycoses and are common. (a) Tinea barbae (barber's itch) occurs on the lower face. (b) Tinea pedis (athlete's foot) occurs on the feet, causing itching, burning, and dry, cracked skin between the toes. (c) A close-up view of tinea corporis (ringworm) caused by Trichophyton mentagrophytes. (credit a, c: modification of work by Centers for Disease Control and Prevention; credit b: modification of work by Al Hasan M, Fitzgerald SM, Saoudian M, Krishnaswamy G)*

Dermatophytes are commonly found in the environment and in soils and are frequently transferred to the skin via contact with other humans and animals. Fungal spores can also spread on hair. Many dermatophytes grow well in moist, dark environments. For example, tinea pedis (athlete's foot) commonly spreads in public showers, and the causative fungi grow well in the dark, moist confines of sweaty shoes and socks. Likewise, tinea cruris (jock itch) often spreads in communal living environments and thrives in warm, moist undergarments. Tineas on the body (tinea corporis) often produce lesions that grow radially and heal towards the center. This causes the formation of a red ring, leading to the misleading name of ringworm.

Eukaryotic Pathogens in Eukaryotic Hosts

When we think about antimicrobial medications, antibiotics such as penicillin often come to mind. Penicillin and related antibiotics interfere with the synthesis of peptidoglycan cell walls, which effectively targets bacterial cells. These antibiotics are useful because humans (like all eukaryotes) do not have peptidoglycan cell walls. Developing medications that are effective against eukaryotic cells but not harmful to human cells is more difficult. Despite huge morphological differences, the cells of humans, fungi, and protists are similar in terms of their ribosomes, cytoskeletons, and cell membranes. As a result, it is more challenging to develop medications that target protozoans and fungi in the same way that antibiotics target prokaryotes.

Fungicides have relatively limited modes of action. Because fungi have ergosterols (instead of cholesterol) in their cell membranes, the different enzymes involved in sterol production can be a target of some medications. The azole and morpholine fungicides interfere with the synthesis of membrane sterols. These are used widely in agriculture (fenpropimorph) and clinically (e.g., miconazole). Some antifungal medications target the chitin cell walls of fungi. Despite the success of these compounds in targeting fungi, antifungal medications for systemic infections still tend to have more toxic side effects than antibiotics for bacteria.

Summary of Cell Structures

Cell Structure	Prokaryotes		Eukaryotes
	Bacteria	**Archaea**	
Size	~0.5–1 μM	~0.5–1 μM	~5–20 μM
Nucleus	No	No	Yes
Genome characteristics	• Single chromosome • Circular • Haploid	• Single chromosome • Circular • Haploid	• Multiple chromosomes • Linear • Haploid or diploid
Cell division	Binary fission	Binary fission	Mitosis, meiosis
Cell wall composition	• Peptidoglycan, or None	• Pseudopeptidoglycan, or Glycopeptide, or Polysaccharide, or Protein (S-layer), or None	• Cellulose (plants, some algae) Chitin (molluscs, insects, crustaceans, and fungi), Silica (some algae), Most others lack cell walls
Motility structures	Rigid spiral flagella composed of flagellin	Rigid spiral flagella composed of archaeal flagellins	Flexible flagella and cilia composed of microtubules
Membrane-bound organelles	No	No	Yes
Ribosomes	70S (relatively small)	70S (relatively small)	• 80S in cytoplasm and rough ER (relatively large) • 70S in mitochondria, chloroplasts

Acellular Pathogens

Viruses

Despite their small size, which prevented them from being seen with light microscopes, the discovery of a filterable component smaller than a bacterium that causes tobacco mosaic disease (TMD) dates back to 1892. At that time, **Dmitri Ivanovski**, a Russian botanist, discovered the source of TMD by using a porcelain filtering device first invented by Charles Chamberland and Louis Pasteur in Paris in 1884. Porcelain Chamberland filters have a pore size of 0.1 μm, which is small enough to remove all bacteria ≥0.2 μm from any liquids passed through the device. An extract obtained from TMD-infected tobacco plants was made to determine the cause of the disease. Initially, the source of the disease was thought to be bacterial. It was surprising to everyone when Ivanovski, using a Chamberland filter, found that the cause of TMD was not removed after passing the extract through the porcelain filter. So if a bacterium was not the cause of TMD, what could be causing the disease? Ivanovski concluded the cause of TMD must be an extremely small bacterium or bacterial spore. Other scientists, including Martinus Beijerinck, continued investigating the

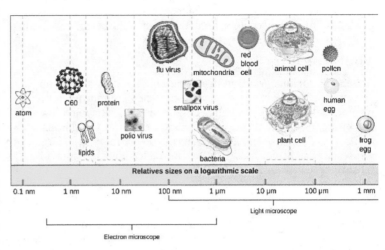

Figure 1 The size of a virus is small relative to the size of most bacterial and eukaryotic cells and their organelles.

cause of TMD. It was Beijerinck, in 1899, who eventually concluded the causative agent was not a bacterium but, instead, possibly a chemical, like a biological poison we would describe today as a toxin. As a result, the word virus, Latin for poison, was used to describe the cause of TMD a few years after Ivanovski's initial discovery. Even though he was not able to see the virus that caused TMD, and did not realize the cause was not a bacterium, Ivanovski is credited as the original discoverer of viruses and a founder of the field of virology.

In 1935, after the development of the electron microscope, **Wendell Stanley** was the first scientist to crystallize the structure of the tobacco mosaic virus and discovered that it is composed of RNA and protein. In 1943, he isolated Influenza B virus, which contributed to the development of an influenza (flu) vaccine. Stanley's discoveries unlocked the mystery of the nature of viruses that had been puzzling scientists for over 40 years and his contributions to the field of virology led to him being awarded the Nobel Prize in 1946.

Today, we can see viruses using electron microscopes and we know much more about them. Viruses are distinct biological entities; however, their evolutionary origin is still a matter of speculation. In terms of taxonomy, they are not included in the tree of life because they are acellular (not consisting of cells). In order to survive and reproduce, viruses must infect a cellular host, making them obligate intracellular parasites. The genome of a virus enters a host cell and directs the production of the viral components, proteins and nucleic acids, needed to form new virus particles called virions. New virions are made in the host cell by assembly of viral components. The new virions transport the viral genome to another host cell to carry out another round of infection.

Characteristics of Viruses
Infectious, acellular pathogens
Obligate intracellular parasites with host and cell-type specificity
DNA or RNA genome (never both)
Genome is surrounded by a protein capsid and, in some cases, a phospholipid membrane (envelope) studded with viral glycoproteins (spikes)
Lack genes for many products needed for successful reproduction, requiring exploitation of host-cell genomes to reproduce

Table 1

Hosts

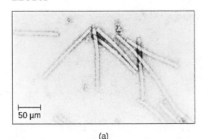

Figure 2 (a) Tobacco mosaic virus (TMV) viewed with transmission electron microscope. (b) Plants infected with tobacco mosaic disease (TMD), caused by TMV. (credit a: modification of work by USDA Agricultural Research Service—scale-bar data from Matt Russell; credit b: modification of work by USDA Forest Service, Department of Plant Pathology Archive North Carolina State University)

Viruses can infect every type of host cell, including those of plants, animals, fungi, protists, bacteria, and archaea. Most viruses will only be able to infect the cells of one or a few species of organism. This is called the **host range**. However, having a wide host range is not common and viruses will typically only infect specific hosts and only specific cell types within those hosts. The viruses that infect bacteria are called **bacteriophages**, or simply phages. The word *phage* comes from the Greek word for devour. Other viruses are just identified by their host group, such as animal or plant viruses. Once a cell is infected, the effects of the virus can vary depending on the type of virus. Viruses may cause abnormal growth of the cell or cell death, alter the cell's genome, or cause little noticeable effect in the cell.

Viral Structures

In general, **virions** (viral particles) are small and cannot be observed using a regular light microscope. They are much smaller than prokaryotic and eukaryotic cells; this is an adaptation allowing viruses to infect these larger cells. The size of a virion can range from 20 nm for small viruses up to 900 nm for typical, large viruses. Recent discoveries, however, have identified new giant viral species with sizes approaching that of a bacterial cell.

As a result of continuing research into the nature of viruses, we now know they consist of a nucleic acid (either RNA or DNA, but never both) surrounded by a protein coat called a **capsid** . The interior of the capsid is not filled with cytosol, as in a cell, but instead it contains the bare necessities in terms of genome and enzymes needed to direct the synthesis of new virions. Each capsid is composed of protein subunits called **capsomeres** made of one or more different types of capsomere proteins that interlock to form the closely packed capsid.

Figure 3 (a) In this transmission electron micrograph, a bacteriophage (a virus that infects bacteria) is dwarfed by the bacterial cell it infects. (b) An illustration of the bacteriophage in the micrograph. (credit a: modification of work by U.S. Department of Energy, Office of Science, LBL, PBD)

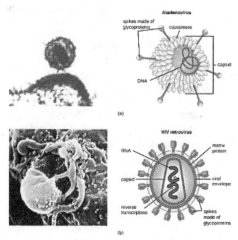

Figure 4 (a) The naked adenovirus uses spikes made of glycoproteins from its capsid to bind to host cells. (b) The enveloped human immunodeficiency virus uses spikes made of glycoproteins embedded in its envelope to bind to host cells (credit a "micrograph": modification of work by NIAID; credit b "micrograph": modification of work by Centers for Disease Control and Prevention

There are two categories of viruses based on general composition. Viruses formed from only a nucleic acid and capsid are called naked viruses or **nonenveloped viruses**. Viruses formed with a nucleic-acid packed capsid surrounded by a lipid layer are called **enveloped viruses**. The **viral envelope** is a small portion of phospholipid membrane obtained as the virion buds from a host cell. The viral envelope may either be intracellular or cytoplasmic in origin.

Extending outward and away from the capsid on some naked viruses and enveloped viruses are protein structures called **spikes**. At the tips of these spikes are structures that allow the virus to attach and enter a cell, like the influenza virus hemagglutinin spikes (H) or enzymes like the neuraminidase (N) influenza virus spikes that allow the virus to detach from the cell surface during release of new virions. Influenza viruses are often identified by their H and N spikes. For example, H1N1 influenza viruses were responsible for the pandemics in 1918 and 2009, H2N2 for the pandemic in 1957, and H3N2 for the pandemic in 1968.

Viruses vary in the shape of their capsids, which can be either **helical**, **polyhedral**, or **complex**. A helical capsid forms the shape of tobacco mosaic virus (TMV), a naked helical virus, and Ebola virus, an enveloped helical virus. The capsid is cylindrical or rod shaped, with the genome fitting just inside the length of the capsid. Polyhedral capsids form the shapes of poliovirus and rhinovirus, and consist of a nucleic acid surrounded by a polyhedral (many-sided) capsid in the form of an icosahedron. An icosahedral capsid is a three-dimensional, 20-sided structure with 12 vertices. These capsids somewhat resemble a soccer ball. Both helical and polyhedral viruses can have envelopes. Viral shapes seen in certain types of bacteriophages, such as T4 phage, and poxviruses, like vaccinia virus, may have features of both polyhedral and helical viruses so they are described as a complex viral shape. In the bacteriophage complex form, the genome is located within the polyhedral head.

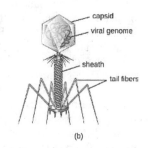

Figure 5 Viral capsids can be (a) helical, (b) polyhedral, or (c) have a complex shape. (credit a "micrograph": modification of work by USDA ARS; credit b "micrograph": modification of work by U.S. Department of Energy)

The Common Cold

The common cold is a generic term for a variety of mild viral infections of the nasal cavity. More than 200 different viruses are known to cause the common cold. The most common groups of cold viruses include rhinoviruses, coronaviruses, and adenoviruses. These infections are widely disseminated in the human population and are transmitted through direct contact and droplet transmission. Coughing and sneezing efficiently produce infectious aerosols, and rhinoviruses are known to persist on environmental surfaces for up to a week.

Viral contact with the nasal mucosa or eyes can lead to infection. Rhinoviruses tend to replicate best between 33 °C (91.4 °F) and 35 °C (95 °F), somewhat below normal body temperature (37 °C [98.6 °F]). As a consequence, they tend to infect the cooler tissues of the nasal cavities. Colds are marked by an irritation of the mucosa that leads to an inflammatory response. This produces common signs and symptoms such as nasal excess nasal secretions (runny nose), congestion, sore throat, coughing, and sneezing. The absence of high fever is typically used to differentiate common colds from other viral infections, like influenza. Some colds may progress to cause otitis media, pharyngitis, or laryngitis, and patients may also experience headaches and body aches. The disease, however, is self-limiting and typically resolves within 1–2 weeks.

There are no effective antiviral treatments for the common cold and antibacterial drugs should not be prescribed unless secondary bacterial infections have been established. Many of the viruses that cause colds are related, so immunity develops throughout life. Given the number of viruses that cause colds, however, individuals are never likely to develop immunity to all causes of the common cold.

Prions

At one time, scientists believed that any infectious particle must contain DNA or RNA. Then, in 1982, **Stanley Prusiner**, a medical doctor studying scrapie (a fatal, degenerative disease in sheep) discovered that the disease was caused by proteinaceous infectious particles, or **prions**. Because proteins are acellular and do not contain DNA or RNA, Prusiner's findings were originally met with resistance and skepticism; however, his research was eventually validated, and he received the Nobel Prize in Physiology or Medicine in 1997.

Prions are responsible for a group of related diseases known as **transmissible spongiform encephalopathies (TSEs)** that occurs in humans and other animals. All TSEs are degenerative, fatal neurological diseases that occur when brain tissue becomes infected by prions. These diseases have a slow onset; symptoms may not become apparent until after an incubation period of years and perhaps decades, but death usually occurs within months to a few years after first symptoms appear.

TSEs in animals include **scrapie,** a disease in sheep that has been known since the 1700s, and **chronic wasting disease**, a disease of deer and elk in the United States and Canada. **Mad cow disease** is seen in cattle and can be transmitted to humans through the consumption of infected nerve tissues. Human prion diseases include **Creutzfeldt-Jakob disease (CJD)** and kuru, a rare disease endemic to Papua New Guinea.

Figure 6 Endogenous normal prion protein (PrPc) is converted into the disease-causing form (PrPsc) when it encounters this variant form of the protein. PrPsc may arise spontaneously in brain tissue, especially if a mutant form of the protein is present, or it may originate from misfolded prions consumed in food that eventually find their way into brain tissue. (credit b: modification of work by USDA)

Prions are typically transmitted by exposure to and ingestion of infected nervous system tissues, tissue transplants, blood transfusions, or contaminated fomites. Prion proteins are normally found in a healthy brain tissue in a form called PrP^C. However, if this protein is misfolded into a denatured form (PrP^{Sc}), it can cause disease. Although the exact function of PrP^C is not currently understood, the protein folds into mostly alpha helices and binds copper. The rogue protein, on the other hand, folds predominantly into beta-pleated sheets and is resistant to proteolysis. In addition, PrP^{Sc} can induce PrP^C to become misfolded and produce more rogue proteins.

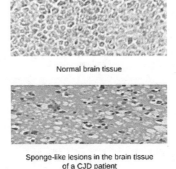

Normal brain tissue

Sponge-like lesions in the brain tissue of a CJD patient

(b)

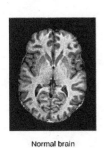

Normal brain   CJD brain

(a)

As PrPSc accumulates, it aggregates and forms fibrils within nerve cells. These protein complexes ultimately cause the cells to die. As a consequence, brain tissues of infected individuals form masses of neurofibrillary tangles and amyloid plaques that give the brain a spongy appearance, which is why these diseases are called **spongiform encephalopathy**. Damage to brain tissue results in a variety of neurological symptoms. Most commonly, affected individuals suffer from memory loss, personality changes, blurred vision, uncoordinated movements, and insomnia. These symptoms gradually worsen over time and culminate in coma and death.

Figure 7 Creutzfeldt-Jakob disease (CJD) is a fatal disease that causes degeneration of neural tissue. (a) These brain scans compare a normal brain to one with CJD. (b) Compared to a normal brain, the brain tissue of a CJD patient is full of sponge-like lesions, which result from abnormal formations of prion protein. (credit a (right): modification of work by Dr. Laughlin Dawes; credit b (top): modification of work by Suzanne Wakim; credit b (bottom): modification of work by Centers for Disease Control and Prevention)

Some Transmissible Spongiform Encephalopathies (TSEs) in Humans	
Disease	Mechanism(s) of Transmission
Variant CJD (vCJD)	Eating contaminated cattle products and by secondary blood borne transmission
Familial CJD (fCJD)	Mutation in germline PrP gene can be inherited
Iatrogenic CJD (iCJD)	Contaminated neurosurgical instruments, corneal graft, gonadotrophic hormone, and, secondarily, by blood transfusion
Kuru	Eating infected meat through ritualistic cannibalism
Fatal familial insomnia (FFI)	Mutation in germline PrP gene

Prions are extremely difficult to destroy because they are resistant to heat, chemicals, and radiation. Even standard sterilization procedures do not ensure the destruction of these particles. Currently, there is no treatment or cure for TSE disease, and contaminated meats or infected animals must be handled according to federal guidelines to prevent transmission.

The gold standard for diagnosing TSE is the histological examination of brain biopsies for the presence of characteristic amyloid plaques, vacuoles, and prion proteins. Great care must be taken by clinicians when handling suspected prion-infected materials to avoid becoming infected themselves. Other tissue assays search for the presence of the 14-3-3 protein, a marker for prion diseases like Creutzfeldt-Jakob disease. New assays, like RT-QuIC (real-time quaking-induced conversion), offer new hope to effectively detect the abnormal prion proteins in tissues earlier in the course of infection. Prion diseases cannot be cured. However, some medications may help slow their progress. Medical support is focused on keeping patients as comfortable as possible despite progressive and debilitating symptoms.

Microbial Metabolism

Throughout earth's history, microbial metabolism has been a driving force behind the development and maintenance of the planet's biosphere. Eukaryotic organisms such as plants and animals typically depend on organic molecules for energy, growth, and reproduction. Prokaryotes, on the other hand, can metabolize a wide range of organic as well as inorganic matter, from complex organic molecules like cellulose to inorganic molecules and ions such as atmospheric nitrogen (N_2), molecular hydrogen (H_2), sulfide (S^{2-}), manganese (II) ions (Mn^{2+}), ferrous iron (Fe^{2+}), and ferric iron (Fe^{3+}), to name a few. By metabolizing such substances, microbes chemically convert them to other forms. In some cases, microbial metabolism produces chemicals that can be harmful to other organisms; in others, it produces substances that are essential to the metabolism and survival of other life forms .

Energy, Matter, and Enzymes

The term used to describe all of the chemical reactions inside a cell is **metabolism**. Cellular processes such as the building or breaking down of complex molecules occur through series of stepwise, interconnected chemical reactions called metabolic pathways. The term **anabolism** refers to those energy-requiring metabolic pathways involved in biosynthesis, converting simple molecular building blocks into more complex molecules, and fueled by the use of cellular energy. Conversely, the term **catabolism** refers to energy-generating pathways that break down complex molecules into simpler ones. Molecular energy stored in the bonds of complex molecules is released in catabolic pathways and harvested in such a way that it can be used to produce high-energy molecules, which are used to drive anabolic pathways. Thus, in terms of energy and molecules, cells are continually balancing catabolism with anabolism.

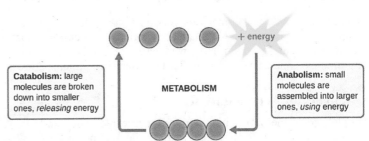

Figure 1 *Metabolism includes catabolism and anabolism. Anabolic pathways require energy to synthesize larger molecules. Catabolic pathways generate energy by breaking down larger molecules. Both types of pathways are required for maintaining the cell's energy balance.*

Energy Carriers: NAD⁺, NADP⁺, FAD, and ATP

A living cell must be able to handle the energy released during catabolism in a way that enables the cell to store energy safely and release it for use only as needed. Living cells accomplish this by using the compound adenosine triphosphate (**ATP**). ATP is often called the "energy currency" of the cell, and, like currency, this versatile compound can be used to fill any energy need of the cell. The removal of a phosphate group from ATP results in the formation of adenosine diphosphate (**ADP**); a lower energy molecule. Adding a phosphate group to a molecule, a process called phosphorylation, requires energy.

In addition to ATP/ADP, there are other important energy carrying molecules in cells. These molecules originate from the B vitamin group and are called nicotinamide adenine dinucleotide (**NAD⁺/NADH**) and flavin adenine dinucleotide (**FAD/FADH₂**). The role of these molecules in metabolism is critical and will be discussed further.

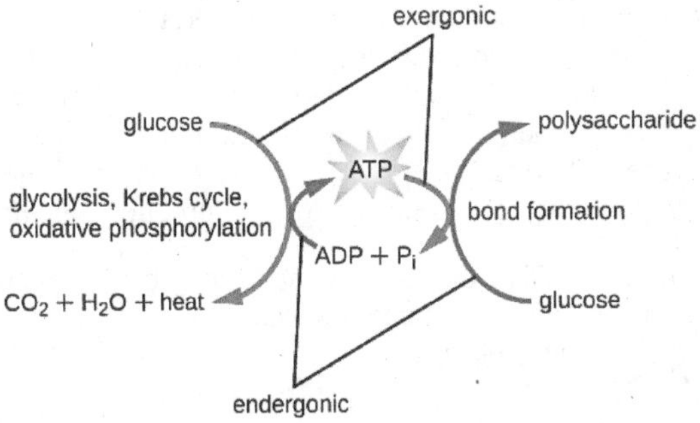

Figure 2 *Energy generating reactions are coupled to energy consuming ones, making the combination favorable. Here, the energy consuming reaction of ATP phosphorylation is coupled to the energy generating reactions of catabolism. Similarly, the energy generating reaction of ATP dephosphorylation is coupled to the energy consuming reaction of polypeptide formation, an example of anabolism.*

Enzyme Structure and Function

A substance that helps speed up a chemical reaction is a **catalyst.** Catalysts are not used or changed during chemical reactions and, therefore, are reusable. Whereas inorganic molecules may serve as catalysts for a wide range of chemical reactions, proteins called **enzymes** serve as catalysts for biochemical reactions inside cells. Enzymes thus play an important role in controlling cellular metabolism.

An enzyme functions by lowering the **activation energy** of a chemical reaction inside the cell. Activation energy is the energy needed to form or break chemical bonds and convert reactants to products. Enzymes lower the activation energy by binding to the reactant molecules and holding them in such a way as to speed up the reaction.

The chemical reactants to which an enzyme binds are called **substrates**, and the location within the enzyme where the substrate binds is called the enzyme's **active site**. The characteristics of the amino acids near the active site create a very specific chemical environment within the active site that induces suitability to binding, albeit briefly, to a specific substrate (or substrates). Due to this jigsaw puzzle-like match between an enzyme and its substrates, enzymes are known for their specificity. Overall, there is a specifically matched enzyme for each substrate and, thus, for each chemical reaction; however, there is some flexibility as well. Some enzymes have the ability to act on several different structurally related substrates.

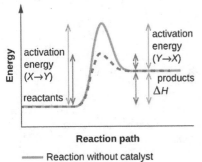

Figure 3 *Enzymes lower the activation energy of a chemical reaction.*

Enzymes are subject to influences by local environmental conditions such as pH, substrate concentration, and temperature. Although increasing the environmental temperature generally increases reaction rates, enzyme catalyzed or otherwise, increasing or decreasing the temperature outside of an optimal range can affect chemical bonds within the active site, making them less well suited to bind substrates. High temperatures will eventually cause enzymes, like other biological molecules, to **denature,** losing their three-dimensional structure and function. Enzymes are also suited to function best within a certain pH range, and, as with temperature, extreme environmental pH values (acidic or basic) can cause enzymes to denature. Active-site amino-acid side chains have their own acidic or basic properties that are optimal for catalysis and, therefore, are sensitive to changes in pH.

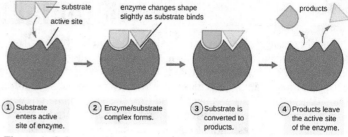

Figure 4 *Substrates bind to an enzyme in the active site to produce a product.*

Overall, enzymes are optimized to work best under the environmental conditions in which the organisms that produce them live. For example, while microbes that inhabit hot springs have enzymes that work best at high temperatures, human pathogens have enzymes that work best at 37°C. Similarly, while enzymes produced by most organisms work best at a neutral pH, microbes growing in acidic environments make enzymes optimized to low pH conditions, allowing for their growth at those conditions.

Discovery of Fermentation

People across the world have enjoyed fermented foods and beverages like beer, wine, bread, yogurt, cheese, and pickled vegetables for all of recorded history. Discoveries from several archeological sites suggest that even prehistoric people took advantage of fermentation to preserve and enhance the taste of food. Archaeologists studying pottery jars from a Neolithic village in China found that people were making a fermented beverage from rice, honey, and fruit as early as 7000 BC.[3]

Production of these foods and beverages requires microbial fermentation, a process that uses bacteria, mold, or yeast to convert sugars (carbohydrates) to alcohol, gases, and organic acids. While it is likely that people first learned about fermentation by accident—perhaps by drinking old milk that had curdled or old grape juice that had fermented—they later learned to harness the power of fermentation to make products like bread, cheese, and wine.

Yeast fermentation yields ethanol and CO_2.

Figure 5 *A microscopic view of Saccharomyces cerevisiae, the yeast responsible for making bread rise (left). Yeast is a microorganism. Its cells metabolize the carbohydrates in flour (middle) and produce carbon dioxide, which causes the bread to rise (right). (credit middle: modification of work by Janus Sandsgaard; credit right: modification of work by "MDreibelbis"/ Flickr)*

Around 1857, Louis Pasteur was able to demonstrate that fermentation was caused by microorganisms. When scientists realized that microorganisms can change food, it led to the exploration into what other things microorganisms are doing, and the start of the Golden Age of Microbiology.

Catabolism of Carbohydrates

Extensive enzyme pathways exist for breaking down carbohydrates to capture energy in ATP bonds. In addition, many catabolic pathways produce intermediate molecules that are also used as building blocks for anabolism. Understanding these processes is important for several reasons. First, because the main metabolic processes involved are common to a wide range of organisms, we can learn a great deal about human metabolism by studying metabolism in more easily manipulated bacteria like *E. coli*. Second, learning about the details of metabolism in these bacteria, including possible differences between bacterial and human pathways, is useful for the diagnosis of pathogens as well as for the discovery of antimicrobial therapies targeting specific pathogens. Last, learning specifically about the pathways involved in metabolism also serves as a basis for comparing other more unusual metabolic strategies used by microbes.

The typical example used to introduce concepts of metabolism to students is carbohydrate catabolism. For humans and many microorganisms, examples of metabolism start with the catabolism of polysaccharides such as glycogen, starch, or cellulose. Enzymes such as amylase, which breaks down glycogen or starch, and cellulases, which break down cellulose, can cause the hydrolysis of glycosidic bonds between the glucose monomers in these polymers, releasing glucose for further catabolism.

Glycolysis

For bacteria, eukaryotes, and most archaea, **glycolysis** is the most common pathway for the catabolism of glucose; it produces energy, reduced electron carriers, and precursor mol-

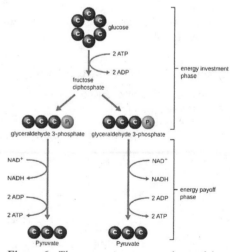

Figure 6 *The energy investment phase of the Embden-Meyerhof-Parnas glycolysis pathway uses two ATP molecules to phosphorylate glucose, forming two glyceraldehyde 3-phosphate (G3P) molecules. The energy payoff phase harnesses the energy in the G3P molecules, producing four ATP molecules, two NADH molecules, and two pyruvates.*

ecules for cellular metabolism. Every living organism carries out some form of glycolysis, suggesting this mechanism is an ancient universal metabolic process. The process itself does not use oxygen; however, glycolysis can be coupled with additional metabolic processes that are either **aerobic** or **anaerobic**. Glycolysis takes place in the cytoplasm of prokaryotic and eukaryotic cells. It begins with a single six-carbon glucose molecule and ends with two molecules of a three-carbon sugar called pyruvate. Pyruvate may be broken down further after glycolysis to harness more energy through aerobic or anaerobic respiration, but many organisms, including many microbes, may be unable to respire; for these organisms, glycolysis may be their only source of generating ATP.

The ATP molecules produced during glycolysis are formed by substrate-level phosphorylation, one of two mechanisms for producing ATP. In substrate-level phosphorylation, a phosphate group is removed from an organic molecule and is directly transferred to an available ADP molecule, producing ATP. During glycolysis, high-energy phosphate groups from the intermediate molecules are added to ADP to make ATP.

Overall, in this process of glycolysis, the net gain from the breakdown of a single glucose molecule is:

- two ATP molecules
- two NADH molecule, and
- two pyruvate molecules.

Transition Reaction and the Krebs Cycle

Glycolysis produces **pyruvate,** which can be further oxidized to capture more energy. For pyruvate to enter the next oxidative pathway, it must first be decarboxylated to a two-carbon acetyl group in the **transition reaction**. In the transition reaction, electrons are also transferred to NAD^+ to form NADH.

The **Krebs cycle** transfers remaining electrons from the acetyl group produced during the transition reaction to electron carrier molecules. Unlike glycolysis, the Krebs cycle is a closed loop: The last part of the pathway regenerates the compound used in the first step. The eight steps of the cycle are a series of chemical reactions that capture the two-carbon acetyl group from the transition reaction, which is added to a four-carbon intermediate in the Krebs cycle, producing the six-carbon intermediate citric acid. As one turn of the cycle returns to the starting point of the four-carbon intermediate, the cycle produces two CO_2 molecules, one ATP molecule produced by substrate-level phosphorylation, and three molecules of NADH and one of $FADH_2$.

Although many organisms use the Krebs cycle as described as part of glucose metabolism, several of the intermediate compounds in the Krebs cycle can be used in synthesizing a wide variety of important cellular molecules, including amino acids, chlorophylls, fatty acids, and nucleotides; therefore, the cycle is both anabolic and catabolic.

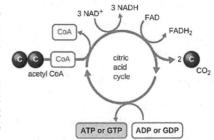

Figure 7 *The Krebs cycle, also known as the citric acid cycle, is summarized here. Note incoming two-carbon acetyl results in the main outputs per turn of two CO_2, three NADH, one $FADH_2$, and one ATP (or GTP) molecules made by substrate-level phosphorylation. Two turns of the Krebs cycle are required to process all of the carbon from one glucose molecule.*

Cellular Respiration

We have just discussed two pathways in glucose catabolism—glycolysis and the Krebs cycle—that generate ATP by substrate-level phosphorylation. Most ATP, however, is generated during a separate process called the **electron transport chain**, which occurs during **cellular respiration**. Cellular respiration begins when electrons are transferred from NADH and $FADH_2$—made in glycolysis, the transition reaction, and the Krebs cycle—through a series of chemical reactions to a final inorganic electron acceptor (either oxygen in aerobic respiration or non-oxygen inorganic molecules in anaerobic respiration). These electron transfers take place on the inner part of the cell membrane of prokaryotic cells or in specialized protein complexes in the inner membrane of the mitochondria of eukaryotic cells. The energy of the electrons is harvested to generate an electrochemical gradient across the membrane, which is used to make ATP by oxidative phosphorylation in the electron transport chain.

Electron Transport Chain

The **electron transport chain (ETC)** is the last component involved in the process of cellular respiration; it comprises a series of membrane-associated protein complexes and associated mobile accessory electron carriers. Electron transport is a series of chemical reactions that resembles a bucket brigade in that electrons from NADH and $FADH_2$ are passed rapidly from one ETC electron carrier to the next.

In **aerobic respiration**, the final electron acceptor at the end of the ETC is an oxygen molecule (O_2) that becomes reduced to water (H_2O) by the final ETC carrier. This electron carrier, cytochrome oxidase, differs between bacterial types and can be used to differentiate closely related bacteria for diagnoses. For example, the gram-negative opportunist *Pseudomonas aeruginosa* and the gram-negative cholera-causing *Vibrio cholerae* use cytochrome c oxidase, which can be detected by the oxidase test, whereas other gram-negative Enterobacteriaceae, like *E. coli*, are negative for this test because they produce different cytochrome oxidase types. In aerobic respiration, oxygen is the **final electron acceptor**.

There are many circumstances under which aerobic respiration is not possible, including any one or more of the following:

- The cell lacks genes encoding an appropriate cytochrome oxidase for transferring electrons to oxygen at the end of the electron transport system.

- The cell lacks genes encoding enzymes to minimize the severely damaging effects of dangerous oxygen radicals produced during aerobic respiration, such as hydrogen peroxide (H_2O_2) or superoxide (O2–).

- The cell lacks a sufficient amount of oxygen to carry out aerobic respiration.

One possible alternative to aerobic respiration is **anaerobic respiration**, using an inorganic molecule other than oxygen as a final electron acceptor. There are many types of anaerobic respiration found in bacteria and archaea. Many aerobically respiring bacteria, including *E. coli*, switch to using nitrate as a final electron acceptor and producing nitrite when oxygen levels have been depleted. Other bacteria use sulfate as a final electron acceptor generating hydrogen sulfide (think rotten egg smell). The largest group of Archea use anaerobic respiration to use carbonate to generate methane. These organisms are found in common anaerobic environments such as swamps (swamp gas), compost piles, and the guts of mammals including humans.

Microbes using anaerobic respiration commonly have an intact Krebs cycle, so these organisms can access the energy of the NADH and $FADH_2$ molecules formed. However, anaerobic respirers use altered ETC carriers encoded by their genomes, including distinct complexes for electron transfer to their final electron acceptors. Smaller electrochemical gradients are generated from these electron transfer systems, so less ATP is formed through anaerobic respiration.

Electron Transport Chain

In each transfer of an electron through the **electron transport chain** (ETC), some energy is stored as potential energy by using it to pump hydrogen ions (H^+) across a membrane. There is an uneven distribution of H^+ across the membrane that establishes an electrochemical gradient because H^+ ions are positively charged (electrical) and there is a higher concentration (chemical) on one side of the membrane. This electrochemical gradient formed by the accumulation of H^+ (also known as a proton) on one side of the membrane compared with the other is referred to as the proton motive force (PMF).

The potential energy of this electrochemical gradient generated by the ETC causes the H^+ to diffuse across a membrane (the plasma membrane in prokaryotic cells and the inner membrane in mitochondria in eukaryotic cells). This flow of hydrogen ions across the membrane, called chemiosmosis, must occur through a channel in the membrane via a membrane-bound enzyme complex called **ATP synthase**. The tendency for movement in this way is much like water accumulated on one side of a dam, moving through the dam when opened. ATP synthase (like a combination of the intake and generator of a hydroelectric dam) is a complex protein that acts as a tiny generator, turning by the force of the H^+ diffusing through the enzyme, down their electrochemical gradient from where there are many mutually repelling H^+ to where there are fewer H^+. The turning of the parts of this molecular machine regenerates ATP from ADP and inorganic phosphate (P_i) by oxidative phosphorylation, a second mechanism for making ATP that harvests the potential energy stored within an electrochemical gradient.

In the simplest description of the ETC, the passage of electrons from NADH and FADH creates potential energy that can be used by the enzyme, ATP synthase, to make ATP.

The number of ATP molecules generated from the catabolism of glucose varies. Overall, the theoretical maximum yield of ATP

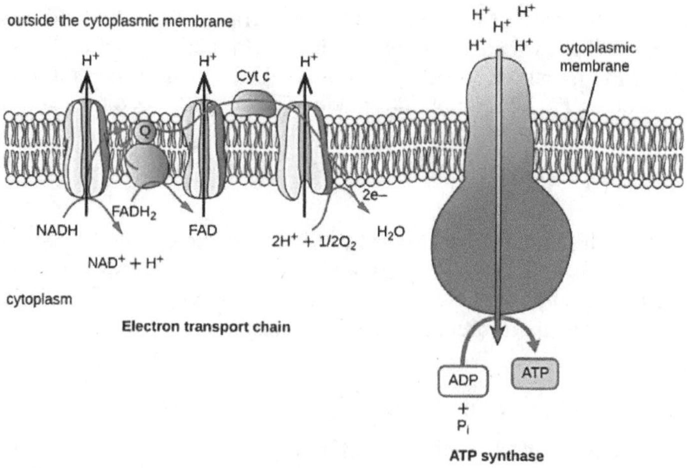

Figure 8 *The bacterial electron transport chain is a series of protein complexes, electron carriers, and ion pumps that is used to pump H^+ out of the bacterial cytoplasm into the extracellular space. H^+ flows back down the electrochemical gradient into the bacterial cytoplasm through ATP synthase, providing the energy for ATP production by oxidative phosphorylation.(credit: modification of work by Klaus Hoffmeier)*

made during the complete aerobic respiration of glucose is 38 molecules, with four being made in glycolysis and the Krebs cycle and 34 being made by the electron transport chain. . In reality, the total ATP yield is usually less, ranging from one to 34 ATP molecules, depending on whether the cell is using aerobic respiration or anaerobic respiration; in eukaryotic cells, some energy is expended to transport intermediates from the cytoplasm into the mitochondria, affecting ATP yield. Also, specific metabolic differences cause many organisms that use anaerobic respiration do not generate as much ATP as those organisms using aerobic respiration.

Source	Carbon Flow	Molecules of Reduced Coenzymes Produced	Net ATP Molecules Made by Substrate-Level Phosphory-lation	Net ATP Molecules Made by Oxidative Phosphory-lation	Theoretical Maximum Yield of ATP Molecules
Glycolysis (EMP)	Glucose (6C) ⟶ 2 pyruvates (3C)	2 NADH	2 ATP	6 ATP from 2 NADH	8
Transition reaction	2 pyruvates (3C) ⟶ 2 acetyl (2C) + 2 CO_2	2 NADH		6 ATP from 2 NADH	6
Krebs cycle	2 acetyl (2C) ⟶ 4 CO_2	6 NADH 2 $FADH_2$	2 ATP	18 ATP from 6 NADH 4 ATP from 2 $FADH_2$	24
Total:	glucose (6C) ⟶ 6 CO_2	10 NADH 2 $FADH_2$	4 ATP	34 ATP	38 ATP

Fermentation

Many cells are unable to carry out respiration because of one or more of the following circumstances:

1. The cell lacks a sufficient amount of oxygen to carry out the ETC using aerobic respiration.

2. The cell lacks genes to make appropriate complexes and electron carriers in the electron transport system.

3. The cell lacks genes to make one or more enzymes in the Krebs cycle.

Whereas lack of an appropriate inorganic final electron acceptor is environmentally dependent, the other two conditions are genetically determined. Thus, many prokaryotes, including members of the clinically important genus *Streptococcus*, are permanently incapable of respiration, even in the presence of oxygen. Conversely, many prokaryotes are facultative, meaning that, should the environmental conditions change to provide an appropriate inorganic final electron acceptor for respiration, organisms containing all the genes required to do so will switch to cellular respiration for glucose metabolism because respiration allows for much greater ATP production per glucose molecule.

If respiration does not occur, NADH must be reoxidized to NAD^+ for reuse as an electron carrier for glycolysis, the cell's only mechanism for producing any ATP, to continue. Some living systems use an organic molecule (commonly pyruvate) as a final electron acceptor through a process called **fermentation**. Fermentation does not involve an electron transport system and does not directly produce any additional ATP beyond that produced during glycolysis by substrate-level phosphorylation. Organisms carrying out fermentation, called fermenters, produce a maximum of two ATP molecules per glucose during glycolysis.

Microbial fermentation processes have been manipulated by humans and are used extensively in the production of various foods and other commercial products, including pharmaceuticals. Microbial fermentation can also be useful for identifying microbes for diagnostic purposes.

Fermentation by some bacteria, like those in yogurt and other soured food products, and by animals in muscles during oxygen depletion, is lactic acid fermentation. Bacteria of several gram-positive genera, including *Lactobacillus*, *Leuconostoc*, and *Streptococcus*, are collectively known as the lactic acid bacteria (LAB), and various strains are important in food production. During yogurt and cheese production, the highly acidic environment generated by lactic acid fermentation denatures proteins contained in milk, causing it to solidify. Lactic acid is the only fermentation product in the case for *Lactobacillus delbrueckii* and *S. thermophiles* used in yogurt production. However, many bacteria produce a mixture of lactic acid, ethanol and/or acetic acid, and CO_2 as a result. One such important fermenter is *Leuconostoc mesenteroides*, which is used for souring vegetables like cucumbers and cabbage, producing pickles and sauerkraut, respectively.

Comparison of Respiration Versus Fermentation

Type of Metabolism	Example	Final Electron Acceptor in ETC	Maximum Yield of ATP Molecules
Aerobic respiration	Pseudomonas aeruginosa	O2	38
Anaerobic respiration	Paracoccus denitrificans Methanobacteriu	$NO^{3-}, SO^{-2}_4, H_2CO2$	1-32
Fermentation	*Candida albicans*	None	2

Lactic acid bacteria are also important medically. The production of low pH environments within the body inhibits the establishment and growth of pathogens in these areas. For example, the vaginal microbiota is composed largely of lactic acid bacteria, but when these bacteria are reduced, yeast can proliferate, causing a yeast infection. Additionally, lactic acid bacteria are important in maintaining the health of the gastrointestinal tract and, as such, are the primary component of probiotics.

Another familiar fermentation process is alcohol fermentation, which produces ethanol. During alcohol fermentation, pyruvate loses a carbon releasing CO_2 gas while producing the two-carbon molecule acetaldehyde. Acetaldehyde is catalyzed by the enzyme alcohol dehydrogenase, transfers an electron from NADH to acetaldehyde, producing ethanol and NAD^+. The ethanol fermentation of pyruvate by the yeast *Saccharomyces cerevisiae* is used in the production of alcoholic beverages and also makes bread products rise due to CO_2 production. Outside of the food industry, ethanol fermentation of plant products is important in biofuel production.

Common Fermentation Pathways			
Pathway	End Products	Example Microbes	Commercial Products
Acetone-buta-nol-ethanol	Acetone, butanol, ethanol, CO_2	Clostridium acetobutyli-cum	Commercial solvents, gasoline alternative
Alcohol	Ethanol, CO_2	Candida, Saccharomyces	Beer, bread
Butanediol	Formic and lactic acid; ethanol; ace-toin; 2,3 butanediol; CO_2; hydrogen gas	Klebsiella, Enterobacter	Chardonnay wine
Butyric acid	Butyric acid, CO_2, hydrogen gas	Clostridium butyricum	Butter
Lactic acid	Lactic acid	Streptococcus, Lactoba-cillus	Sauerkraut, yogurt, cheese
Mixed acid	Acetic, formic, lactic, and succinic acids; ethanol, CO_2, hydrogen gas	Escherichia, Shigella	Vinegar, cosmetics, phar-maceuticals
Propionic acid	Acetic acid, propionic acid, CO_2	Propionibacterium, Bifido-bacterium	Swiss cheese

Beyond lactic acid fermentation and alcohol fermentation, many other fermentation methods occur in prokaryotes, all for the purpose of ensuring an adequate supply of NAD^+ for glycolysis. Without these pathways, glycolysis would not occur and no ATP would be harvested from the breakdown of glucose. It should be noted that most forms of fermentation produce gas, commonly CO_2 and/or hydrogen gas. Many of these different types of fermentation pathways are also used in food production and each results in the production of different organic acids, contributing to the unique flavor of a particular fermented food product. The propionic acid produced during propionic acid fermentation contributes to the distinctive flavor of Swiss cheese, for example.

Several fermentation products are important commercially outside of the food industry. For example, chemical solvents such as acetone and butanol are produced during acetone-butanol-ethanol fermentation. Complex organic pharmaceutical compounds used in antibiotics (e.g., penicillin), vaccines, and vitamins are produced through mixed acid fermentation. Fermentation products are used in the laboratory to differentiate various bacteria for diagnostic purposes. For example, enteric bacteria are known for their ability to perform mixed acid fermentation, reducing the pH, which can be detected using a pH indicator. Similarly, the bacterial production of acetoin during butanediol fermentation can also be detected. Gas production from fermentation can also be seen in an inverted Durham tube that traps produced gas in a broth culture.

Microbes can also be differentiated according to the substrates they can ferment. For example, *E. coli* can ferment lactose, forming gas, whereas some of its close gram-negative relatives cannot. The ability to ferment the sugar alcohol sorbitol is used to identify the patho-genic enterohemorrhagic O157:H7 strain of *E. coli* because, unlike other *E. coli* strains, it is unable to ferment sorbitol. Last, mannitol fermentation differentiates the mannitol-fermenting *Staphylococcus aureus* from other non–mannitol-fermenting staphylococci.

Identification of Microorganisms Using Biochemistry

Accurate identification of bacterial isolates is essential in a clinical microbiology laboratory because the results often inform decisions about treatment that directly affect patient outcomes. For example, cases of food poisoning require accurate identification of the caus-ative agent so that physicians can prescribe appropriate treatment. Likewise, it is important to accurately identify the causative pathogen during an outbreak of disease so that appropriate strategies can be employed to contain the epidemic.

There are many ways to detect, characterize, and identify microorganisms. Some methods rely on phenotypic biochemical character-istics, while others use genotypic identification. The biochemical characteristics of a bacterium provide many traits that are useful for classification and identification. Analyzing the nutritional and metabolic capabilities of the bacterial isolate is a common approach for determining the genus and the species of the bacterium.

Identifying Bacteria Using Multitest Panels

Identification of a microbial isolate is essential for the proper diagnosis and appropriate treatment of patients. Scientists have developed techniques that identify bacteria according to their biochemical characteristics. Typically, they either examine the use of specific carbon sources as substrates for fermentation or other metabolic reactions, or they identify fermentation products or specific enzymes present in reactions. In the past, microbiologists have used individual test tubes and plates to conduct biochemical testing. However, scientists, especially those in clinical laboratories, now more frequently use plastic, disposable, multitest panels that contain a number of miniature reaction tubes, each typically including a specific substrate and pH indicator. After inoculation of the test panel with a small sample of the microbe in question and incubation, scientists can compare the results to a database that includes the expected results for specific bio-chemical reactions for known microbes, thus enabling rapid identification of a sample microbe. These test panels have allowed scientists to reduce costs while improving efficiency and reproducibility by performing a larger number of tests simultaneously.

Many commercial, miniaturized biochemical test panels cover a number of clinically important groups of bacteria and yeasts. One of the earliest and most popular test panels is the Analytical Profile Index (API) panel invented in the 1970s. Once some basic laboratory characterization of a given strain has been performed, such as determining the strain's Gram morphology, an appropriate test strip that contains 10 to 20 different biochemical tests for differentiating strains within that microbial group can be used. Currently, the various API strips can be used to quickly and easily identify more than 600 species of bacteria, both aerobic and anaerobic, and approximately 100 different types of yeasts. Based on the colors of the reactions when metabolic end products are present, due to the presence of pH indicators, a metabolic profile is created from the result. Microbiologists can then compare the sample's profile to the database to identify the specific microbe.

Figure 9 *The API 20NE test strip is used to identify specific strains of gram-negative bacteria outside the Enterobacteriaceae. Here is an API 20NE test strip result for Photobacterium damselae ssp. piscicida.*

Microbial Growth

Osmosis

In most prokaryotic cells, morphology is maintained by the cell wall in combination with cytoskeletal elements. The cell wall is a structure found in most prokaryotes and some eukaryotes; it envelopes the cell membrane, protecting the cell from changes in **osmotic pressure**. Osmotic pressure occurs because of differences in the concentration of solutes on opposing sides of a semipermeable membrane. Water is able to pass through a semipermeable membrane, but solutes (dissolved molecules like salts, sugars, and other compounds) cannot. When the concentration of solutes is greater on one side of the membrane, water diffuses across the membrane from the side with the lower concentration (more water) to the side with the higher concentration (less water) until the concentrations on both sides become equal. This diffusion of water is called **osmosis**, and it can cause extreme osmotic pressure on a cell when its external environment changes.

The external environment of a cell can be described as an **isotonic**, **hypertonic**, or **hypotonic** medium. In an isotonic medium, the solute concentrations inside and outside the cell are approximately equal, so there is no net movement of water across the cell membrane. In a hypertonic medium, the solute concentration outside the cell exceeds that inside the cell, so water diffuses out of the cell and into the external medium. In a hypotonic medium, the solute concentration inside the cell exceeds that outside of the cell, so water will move by osmosis into the cell. This causes the cell to swell and potentially lyse, or burst.

The degree to which a particular cell is able to withstand changes in osmotic pressure is called tonicity. Cells that have a cell wall are better able to withstand subtle changes in osmotic pressure and maintain their shape. In hypertonic environments, cells that lack a cell wall can become dehydrated, causing crenation, or shriveling of the cell; the plasma membrane contracts and appears scalloped or notched. By contrast, cells that possess a cell wall undergo plasmolysis rather than crenation. In plasmolysis, the plasma membrane contracts and detaches from the cell wall, and there is a decrease in interior volume, but the cell wall remains intact, thus allowing the cell to maintain some shape and integrity for a period of time. Likewise, cells that lack a cell wall are more prone to lysis in hypotonic environments. The presence of a cell wall allows the cell to maintain its shape and integrity without lysing.

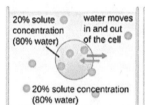

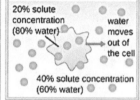

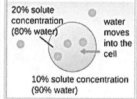

(a) Isotonic solution
A solution that has the *same* solute concentration as another solution. There is no net movement of water particles, and the overall concentration on both sides of the cell membrane remains constant.

(b) Hypertonic solution
A solution that has a *higher* solute concentration than another solution. Water particles will move out of the cell, causing crenation.

(c) Hypotonic solution
A solution that has a *lower* solute concentration than another solution. Water particles will move into the cell, causing the cell to expand and eventually lyse.

How Microbes Grow

Microbial growth describes the growth of the number of cells in a population, not the size of an individual cell. The bacterial cell cycle involves the formation of new cells through the replication of DNA and partitioning of cellular components into two daughter cells. In prokaryotes, reproduction is always asexual.

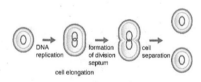

Binary Fission

Since most bacteria have only a single circular chromosome, the division of a bacterial cell is relatively simple compared to mitosis in eukaryotic cells that allows for the sorting and proper distribution of many chromosomes. The most common mechanism of cell division in bacteria is a process called **binary fission**.

Figure 1 *(a) The electron micrograph depicts two cells of Salmonella typhimurium after a binary fission event. (b) Binary fission in bacteria starts with the replication of DNA as the cell elongates. A division septum forms in the center of the cell. Two daughter cells of similar size form and separate, each receiving a copy of the original chromosome. (credit a: modification of work by Centers for Disease Control and Prevention)*

Generation Time

In prokaryotes (Bacteria and Archaea), the **generation time** is also called the **doubling time** and is defined as the time it takes for the population to double through one round of binary fission. Bacterial doubling times vary enormously. Whereas *Escherichia coli* can double in as little as 20 minutes under optimal growth conditions in the laboratory, bacteria of the same species may need several days to double in especially harsh environments. Most pathogens grow rapidly, like *E. coli*, but there are exceptions. For example, *Mycobacterium tuberculosis*, the causative agent of tuberculosis, has a generation time of between 15 and 20 hours. On the other hand, *M. leprae*, which causes Hansen's disease (leprosy), grows much more slowly, with a doubling time of 14 days.

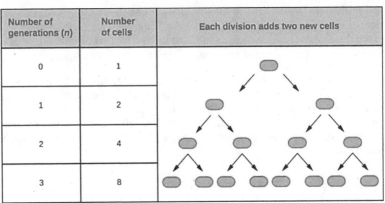

Number of generations (n)	Number of cells	Each division adds two new cells
0	1	
1	2	
2	4	
3	8	

Figure 2 *The parental cell divides and gives rise to two daughter cells. Each of the daughter cells, in turn, divides, giving a total of four cells in the second generation and eight cells in the third generation. Each division doubles the number of cells.*

The Growth Curve

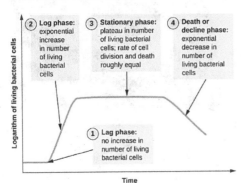

Figure 3 *The growth curve of a bacterial culture is represented by the logarithm of the number of live cells plotted as a function of time. The graph can be divided into four phases according to the slope, each of which matches events in the cell. The four phases are lag, log, stationary, and death.*

Microorganisms grown in closed culture (also known as a batch culture), in which no nutrients are added and most waste is not removed, follow a reproducible growth pattern referred to as the **growth curve**. An example of a batch culture in nature is a pond in which a small number of cells grow in a closed environment. In a closed environment, the culture density is also a measure of the number of cells in the population. Infections of the body do not always follow the growth curve, but correlations can exist depending upon the site and type of infection. When the number of live cells is plotted against time, distinct phases can be observed in the curve.

The beginning of the growth curve represents a small number of cells, referred to as an **inoculum,** that are added to a fresh **culture medium**, a nutritional broth that supports growth. The initial phase of the growth curve is called the **lag phase**, during which cells are gearing up for the next phase of growth. The number of cells does not change during the lag phase; however, cells grow larger and are metabolically active, synthesizing proteins needed to grow within the medium. If any cells were damaged or shocked during the transfer to the new medium, repair takes place during the lag phase. The duration of the lag phase is determined by many factors, including the species and genetic make-up of the cells, the composition of the medium, and the size of the original inoculum.

In **the logarithmic (log) growth phase**, sometimes called exponential growth phase, the cells are actively dividing by binary fission and their number increases exponentially. For any given bacterial species, the generation time under specific growth conditions (nutrients, temperature, pH, and so forth) is genetically determined. During the log phase, the relationship between time and number of cells is not linear but exponential; however, the growth curve is often plotted on a semi logarithmic graph which gives the appearance of a linear relationship.

Cells in the log phase show constant growth rate and uniform metabolic activity. For this reason, cells in the log phase are preferentially used for industrial applications and research work. The log phase is also the stage where bacteria are the most susceptible to the action of disinfectants and common antibiotics that affect protein, DNA, and cell-wall synthesis.

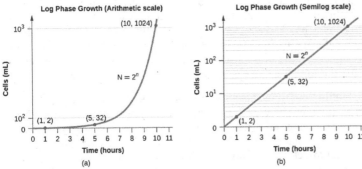

Figure 4 *Both graphs illustrate population growth during the log phase for a bacterial sample with an initial population of one cell and a doubling time of 1 hour. (a) When plotted on an arithmetic scale, the growth rate resembles a curve. (b) When plotted on a semilogarithmic scale (meaning the values on the y-axis are logarithmic), the growth rate appears linear.*

As the number of cells increases through the log phase, several factors contribute to a slowing of the growth rate. Waste products accumulate and nutrients are gradually used up. In addition, gradual depletion of oxygen begins to limit aerobic cell growth. This combination of unfavorable conditions slows and finally stalls population growth. The total number of live cells reaches a plateau referred to as the **stationary phase** . In this phase, the number of new cells created by cell division is now equivalent to the number of cells dying; thus, the total population of living cells is relatively stagnant. The culture density in a stationary culture is constant. The culture's carrying capacity, or maximum culture density, depends on the types of microorganisms in the culture and the specific conditions of the culture; however, carrying capacity is constant for a given organism grown under the same conditions.

During the stationary phase, cells switch to a survival mode of metabolism. As growth slows, so too does the synthesis of peptidoglycans, proteins, and nucleic-acids; thus, stationary cultures are less susceptible to antibiotics that disrupt these processes. In bacteria capable of producing endospores, many cells undergo sporulation during the stationary phase. Secondary metabolites, including antibiotics, are synthesized in the stationary phase. In certain pathogenic bacteria, the stationary phase is also associated with the expression of virulence factors, products that contribute to a microbe's ability to survive, reproduce, and cause disease in a host organism. For example, *Staphylococcus aureus* initiates the production of enzymes that can break down human tissue and cellular debris, clearing the way for bacteria to spread to new tissue where nutrients are more plentiful.

As a culture medium accumulates toxic waste and nutrients are exhausted, cells die in greater and greater numbers. Soon, the number of dying cells exceeds the number of dividing cells, leading to an exponential decrease in the number of cells. This is the aptly named **death phase**, sometimes called the decline phase. Many cells lyse and release nutrients into the medium, allowing surviving cells to maintain viability and form endospores. A few cells, the so-called persisters, are characterized by a slow metabolic rate. Persister cells are medically important because they are associated with certain chronic infections, such as tuberculosis, that do not respond to antibiotic treatment.

Biofilms

A **biofilm** is a complex community of one or more microorganism species, typically forming as a slimy coating attached to a surface because of the production of an **extrapolymeric substance (EPS) (or slime layer)** that attaches to a surface or at the interface between surfaces (e.g., between air and water). In nature, biofilms are abundant and frequently occupy complex niches within ecosystems. In medicine, biofilms can coat medical devices and exist within the body. Because they possess unique characteristics, such as increased resistance against the immune system and to antimicrobial drugs, biofilms are of particular interest to microbiologists and clinicians alike.

Because biofilms are thick, they cannot be observed very well using light microscopy; slicing a biofilm to create a thinner specimen might kill or disturb the microbial community. Confocal microscopy provides clearer images of biofilms because it can focus on one z-plane at a time and produce a three-dimensional image of a thick specimen. In nature, microorganisms grow mainly in **biofilms**, complex and dynamic ecosystems that form on a variety of environmental surfaces,

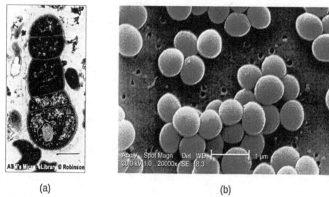

(a)   (b)

Figure 6 *Stages in the formation and life cycle of a biofilm. (credit: modification of work by Public Library of Science and American Society for Microbiology)*

from industrial conduits and water treatment pipelines to rocks in river beds. Biofilms are not restricted to solid surface substrates, however. Almost any surface in a liquid environment containing some minimal nutrients will eventually develop a biofilm. Microbial mats that float on water, for example, are biofilms that contain large populations of photosynthetic microorganisms. Biofilms found in the human mouth may contain hundreds of bacterial species. Regardless of the environment where they occur, biofilms are not random collections of microorganisms; rather, they are highly structured communities that provide a selective advantage to their constituent microorganisms.

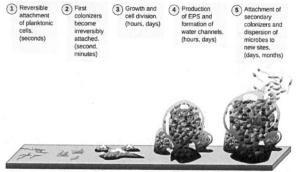

Figure 5 *(a) This TEM image of cells in a biofilm shows well-defined internal structures of the cells because of varying levels of opacity in the specimen. (b) This color-enhanced SEM image of the bacterium Staphylococcus aureus illustrates the ability of scanning electron microscopy to render three-dimensional images of the surface structure of cells. (credit a: modification of work by American Society for Microbiology; credit b: modification of work by Centers for Disease Control and Prevention)*

Free-floating microbial cells that live in an aquatic environment are called planktonic cells. The formation of a biofilm essentially involves the attachment of planktonic cells to a substrate, where they become sessile (attached to a surface). This occurs in stages. The first stage involves the attachment of planktonic cells to a surface coated with a conditioning film of organic material. At this point, attachment to the substrate is reversible, but as cells express new phenotypes that facilitate the formation of slime layers, they transition from a planktonic to a sessile lifestyle. The biofilm develops characteristic structures, including an extensive matrix and water channels. Appendages such as fimbriae, pili, and flagella interact with the slime layers, and microscopy and genetic analysis suggest that such structures are required for the establishment of a mature biofilm. In the last stage of the biofilm life cycle, cells on the periphery of the biofilm revert to a planktonic lifestyle, sloughing off the mature biofilm to colonize new sites. This stage is referred to as dispersal.

Within a biofilm, different species of microorganisms establish metabolic collaborations in which the waste product of one organism becomes the nutrient for another. For example, aerobic microorganisms consume oxygen, creating anaerobic regions that promote the growth of anaerobes. This occurs in many polymicrobial infections that involve both aerobic and anaerobic pathogens.

The human body harbors many types of biofilms, some beneficial and some harmful. For example, the layers of normal microbiota lining the intestinal and respiratory mucosa play a role in warding off infections by pathogens. However, other biofilms in the body can have a detrimental effect on health. For example, the plaque that forms on teeth is a biofilm that can contribute to dental and periodontal disease. Biofilms can also form in wounds, sometimes causing serious infections that can spread. The bacterium *Pseudomonas aeruginosa* often colonizes biofilms in the airways of patients with cystic fibrosis, causing chronic and sometimes fatal infections of the lungs. Biofilms can also form on medical devices used in or on the body, causing infections in patients with in-dwelling catheters, artificial joints, or contact lenses.

Pathogens embedded within biofilms exhibit a higher resistance to antibiotics than their free-floating counterparts. Several hypotheses have been proposed to explain why. Cells in the deep layers of a biofilm are metabolically inactive and may be less susceptible to the action of antibiotics that disrupt metabolic activities. The EPS may also slow the diffusion of antibiotics and antiseptics, preventing them from reaching cells in the deeper layers of the biofilm. Phenotypic changes may also contribute to the increased resistance exhibited by bacterial cells in biofilms. For example, the increased production of efflux pumps, membrane-embedded proteins that actively extrude antibiotics out of bacterial cells, have been shown to be an important mechanism of antibiotic resistance among biofilm-associated bacteria. Finally, biofilms provide an ideal environment for the exchange of extrachromosomal DNA, which often includes genes that confer antibiotic resistance.

Chemical Requirements for Microbial Growth

Classification by Carbon and Energy Source

Organisms can be identified according to the source of carbon they use for metabolism as well as their energy source. The prefixes auto- ("self") and hetero- ("other") refer to the origins of the carbon sources various organisms can use. Organisms that convert inorganic carbon dioxide (CO_2) into organic carbon compounds are **autotrophs.** Plants and cyanobacteria are well-known examples of autotrophs. Conversely, **heterotrophs** rely on more complex organic carbon compounds as nutrients; these are provided to them initially by autotrophs. Many organisms, ranging from humans to many prokaryotes, including the well-studied *Escherichia coli*, are heterotrophic.

Carbon Cycle

Carbon is one of the most important elements to living organisms, as shown by its abundance and presence in all organic molecules. The carbon cycle exemplifies the connection between organisms in various ecosystems. Carbon is exchanged between heterotrophs and autotrophs within and between ecosystems primarily by way of atmospheric CO_2, a fully oxidized version of carbon that serves as the basic building block that autotrophs use to build multicarbon, high-energy organic molecules such as glucose. Photosynthesizers harness energy from the sun and from inorganic chemical compounds, respectively, to covalently bond carbon atoms together into reduced organic compounds whose energy can be later accessed through the processes of respiration and fermentation.

Overall, there is a constant exchange of CO_2 between the heterotrophs (which produce CO_2 as a result of respiration or fermentation) and the autotrophs (which use the CO_2 for fixation). Autotrophs also respire or ferment, consuming the organic molecules they form; they do not fix carbon for heterotrophs, but rather use it for their own metabolic needs.

Nitrogen Cycle

Many biological macromolecules, including proteins and nucleic acids, contain nitrogen; however, getting nitrogen into living organisms is difficult. Prokaryotes play essential roles in the nitrogen cycle , transforming nitrogen between various forms for their own needs, benefiting other organisms indirectly. Plants and phytoplankton cannot incorporate nitrogen from the atmosphere (where it exists as tightly bonded, triple covalent N_2), even though this molecule composes approximately 78% of the atmosphere. Nitrogen enters the living world through free-living and symbiotic bacteria, which incorporate nitrogen into their macromolecules through specialized biochemical pathways called **nitrogen fixation**. Plants and animals rely heavily on prokaryotes for nitrogen fixation, the conversion of atmospheric nitrogen into ammonia, a compound that some plants can use to form many different biomolecules necessary to their survival. Bacteria in the genus *Rhizobium*, for example, are nitrogen-fixing bacteria; they live in the roots of legume plants such as clover, alfalfa, and peas Ammonia produced by *Rhizobium* helps these plants to survive by enabling them to make building blocks of nucleic acids. In turn, these plants may be eaten by animals—sustaining their growth and survival—or they may die, in which case the products of nitrogen fixation will enrich the soil and be used by other plants.

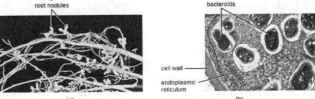

Figure 7 *(a) Nitrogen-fixing bacteria such as Rhizobium live in the root nodules of legumes such as clover. (b) This micrograph of the root nodule shows bacteroids (bacterium-like cells or modified bacterial cells) within the plant cells. The bacteroids are visible as darker ovals within the larger plant cell. (credit a: modification of work by USDA)*

Oxygen Requirements for Microbial Growth

Aerobic respiration constantly generates reactive oxygen species (ROS) called **superoxide free radicals** (or just free radicals) and **hydrogen peroxide**, byproducts that must be detoxified. ROS interact with all the normal molecules in the cell and cause significant damage and potential death. Even organisms that do not use aerobic respiration need some way to break down some of the ROS that may form from atmospheric oxygen. Two main enzymes break down those toxic byproducts: **superoxide dismutase (SOD)** and **catalase**.

The enzymes play an important role by limiting the damage caused by ROS. The enzyme superoxide dismutase (SOD) and breaks down the powerful superoxide free radicals generated by aerobic metabolism:

$(2)O_2^- + 2H^+ \rightarrow H_2O_2 + O_2$

The enzyme catalase converts hydrogen peroxide to water and oxygen.

$2H_2O_2 \rightarrow 2H_2O + O_2$

Without these important enzymes, cells cannot survive in an environment that contains oxygen.

We can easily observe different requirements for molecular oxygen by growing bacteria in a special medium (called thioglycolate) that upon autoclaving flushes out most of the oxygen. The tubes are inoculated with the bacterial cultures to be tested and incubated at an appropriate temperature. Over time, oxygen slowly diffuses throughout the tube culture from the top. Bacterial density increases in the area where oxygen concentration is best suited for the growth of that particular organism.

The growth of bacteria with varying oxygen requirements in tubes is illustrated in the figure. In tube A, all the growth is seen at the top of the tube. The bacteria are **obligate (strict) aerobes** that cannot grow without an abundant supply of oxygen. Tube B looks like the opposite of tube A. Bacteria grow at the bottom of tube B. Those are **obligate anaerobes**, which are killed by oxygen. Tube C shows heavy growth at the top of the tube and growth throughout the tube, a typical result with **facultative anaerobes**. Facultative anaerobes are organisms that thrive in the presence of oxygen but also grow in its absence by relying on fermentation or anaerobic respiration, if there is a suitable electron acceptor other than oxygen and the organism is able to perform anaerobic respiration. The **aerotolerant anaerobes** in tube D are indifferent to the presence of oxy-

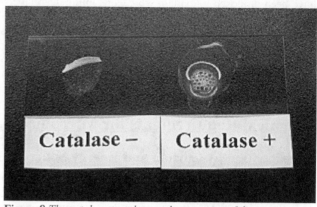

Figure 8 *The catalase test detects the presence of the enzyme catalase by noting whether bubbles are released when hydrogen peroxide is added to a culture sample. Compare the positive result (right) with the negative result (left). (credit: Centers for Disease Control and Prevention)*

gen. They do not use oxygen because they usually have a fermentative metabolism, but they are not harmed by the presence of oxygen as obligate anaerobes are. Tube E on the right shows a "Goldilocks" culture. The oxygen level has to be just right for growth, not too much and not too little. These **microaerophiles** are bacteria that require a minimum level of oxygen for growth, about 1%–10%, well below the 21% found in the atmosphere.

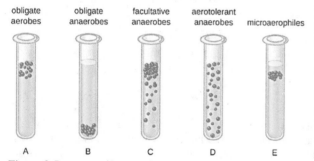

Figure 9 *Diagram of bacterial cell distribution in thioglycolate tubes.*

Examples of obligate aerobes are *Mycobacterium tuberculosis*, the causative agent of tuberculosis and *Micrococcus luteus*, a gram-positive bacterium that colonizes the skin. *Neisseria meningitidis*, the causative agent of severe bacterial meningitis, and *N. gonorrhoeae*, the causative agent of sexually transmitted gonorrhea, are also obligate aerobes.

Many obligate anaerobes are found in the environment where anaerobic conditions exist, such as in deep sediments of soil, still waters, and at the bottom of the deep ocean where there is no photosynthetic life. Anaerobic conditions also exist naturally in the intestinal tract of animals. Obligate anaerobes, mainly *Bacteroidetes*, represent a large fraction of the microbes in the human gut. Transient anaerobic conditions exist when tissues are not supplied with blood circulation; they die and become an ideal breeding ground for obligate anaerobes. Another type of obligate anaerobe encountered in the human body is the gram-positive, rod-shaped *Clostridium* spp. Their ability to form endospores allows them to survive in the presence of oxygen. One of the major causes of health-acquired infections is *C. difficile*, known as C. diff. Prolonged use of antibiotics for other infections increases the probability of a patient developing a secondary *C. difficile* infection. Antibiotic treatment disrupts the balance of microorganisms in the intestine and allows the colonization of the gut by *C. difficile*, causing a significant inflammation of the colon.

Other clostridia responsible for serious infections include *C. tetani*, the agent of tetanus, and *C. perfringens*, which causes gas gangrene. In both cases, the infection starts in necrotic tissue (dead tissue that is not supplied with oxygen by blood circulation). This is the reason that deep puncture wounds are associated with tetanus. When tissue death is accompanied by lack of circulation, gangrene is always a danger.

Figure 10 Anaerobic environments are still common on earth. They include environments like (a) a bog where undisturbed dense sediments are virtually devoid of oxygen, and (b) the rumen (first compartment of the cow's stomach), which provides an oxygen-free incubator for methanogens and other obligate anaerobic bacteria 9credit a: modification of work by National Park Service; credit b: modification of work by US Department of Agriculture.

Staphylococci and Enterobacteriaceae are examples of facultative anaerobes. Staphylococci are found on the skin and upper respiratory tract. Enterobacteriaceae are found primarily in the gut and upper respiratory tract but can sometimes spread to the urinary tract, where they are capable of causing infections. It is not unusual to see mixed bacterial infections in which the facultative anaerobes use up the oxygen, creating an environment for the obligate anaerobes to flourish.

Examples of aerotolerant anaerobes include lactobacilli and streptococci, both found in the oral microbiota. *Campylobacter jejuni*, which causes gastrointestinal infections, is an example of a microaerophile and is grown under low-oxygen conditions.

When looking for catalase and SOD, obligate anaerobes usually lack these enzymes. All the others because they grow in the presence of oxygen, must have at least some SOD and catalase. Aerotolerant anaerobes have SOD but not catalase. The catalase test is the basis of a useful and rapid test to distinguish streptococci, which are aerotolerant and do not possess catalase, from staphylococci, which are facultative anaerobes.

The Effects of pH on Microbial Growth

Yogurt, pickles, sauerkraut, and lime-seasoned dishes all owe their tangy taste to a high acid content. Recall that acidity is a function of the concentration of hydrogen ions [H⁺] and is measured as pH. Environments with pH values below 7.0 are considered acidic, whereas those with pH values above 7.0 are considered basic. Extreme pH affects the structure of all macromolecules. But the component most sensitive to pH in the cell is its workhorse, the protein. Moderate changes in pH promote denaturation and destroy activity.

The **optimum growth pH** is the most favorable pH for the growth of an organism. The lowest pH value that an organism can tolerate is called the **minimum growth pH** and the highest pH is **the maximum growth pH**. These values can cover a wide range, which is important for the preservation of food and to microorganisms' survival in the stomach. For example, the optimum growth pH of *Salmonella* spp. is 7.0–7.5, but the minimum growth pH is closer to 4.2.

Figure 11 *Lactic acid bacteria that ferment milk into yogurt or transform vegetables in pickles thrive at a pH close to 4.0. Sauerkraut and dishes such as pico de gallo owe their tangy flavor to their acidity. Acidic foods have been a mainstay of the human diet for centuries, partly because most microbes that cause food spoilage grow best at a near neutral pH and do not tolerate acidity well. (credit "yogurt": modification of work by "nina.jsc"/Flickr; credit "pickles": modification of work by Noah Sussman; credit "sauerkraut": modification of work by Jesse LaBuff; credit "pico de gallo": modification of work by "regan76"/Flickr)*

Most bacteria are **neutrophiles**, meaning they grow optimally at a pH within one or two pH units of the neutral pH of 7. Most familiar bacteria, like *Escherichia coli*, staphylococci, and *Salmonella* spp. are neutrophiles and do not fare well in the acidic pH of the stomach.

Microorganisms that grow optimally at pH less than 5.55 are called **acidophiles**. For example, the sulfur-oxidizing *Sulfolobus* spp. isolated from sulfur mud fields and hot springs in Yellowstone National Park are extreme acidophiles. These archaea survive at pH values of 2.5–3.5. Species of the archaean genus *Ferroplasma* live in acid mine drainage at pH values of 0–2.9. *Lactobacillus* bacteria, which are an important part of the normal microbiota of the vagina, can tolerate acidic environments at pH values 3.5–6.8 and also contribute to the acidity of the vagina (pH of 4) through their metabolic production of lactic acid. The vagina's acidity plays an important role in inhibiting other microbes that are less tolerant of acidity.

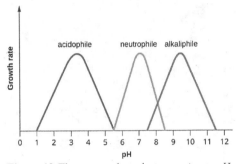

Figure 12 *The curves show the approximate pH ranges for the growth of the different classes of pH-specific prokaryotes. Each curve has an optimal pH and extreme pH values at which growth is much reduced. Most bacteria are neutrophiles and grow best at near-neutral pH (center curve). Acidophiles have optimal growth at pH values near 3 and alkaliphiles have optimal growth at pH values above 9.*

Temperature and Microbial Growth

When the exploration of Lake Whillans started in Antarctica, researchers did not expect to find much life. Constant subzero temperatures and lack of obvious sources of nutrients did not seem to be conditions that would support a thriving ecosystem. To their surprise, the samples retrieved from the lake showed abundant microbial life. In a different but equally harsh setting, bacteria grow at the bottom of the ocean in sea vents, where temperatures can reach 340 °C (700 °F).

Microbes can be roughly classified according to the range of temperature at which they can grow. The growth rates are the highest at the **optimum growth temperature** for the organism. The lowest temperature at which the organism can survive and replicate is its **minimum growth temperature**. The highest temperature at which growth can occur is its **maximum growth temperature**. The following ranges of permissive growth temperatures are approximate only and can vary according to other environmental factors.

Organisms categorized as **mesophiles** ("middle loving") are adapted to moderate temperatures, with optimal growth temperatures ranging from room temperature (about 20 °C) to about 45 °C. As would be expected from the core temperature of the human body, 37 °C (98.6 °F), normal human microbiota and pathogens (e.g., *E. coli*, *Salmonella* spp., and *Lactobacillus* spp.) are mesophiles.

The organisms retrieved from arctic lakes such as Lake Whillans are considered extreme psychrophiles (cold loving). **Psychrophiles** are microorganisms that can grow at 0 °C and below, have an optimum growth temperature close to 15 °C, and usually do not survive at temperatures above 20 °C. They are found in permanently cold environments such as the deep waters of the oceans. Because they are active at low temperature, psychrophiles are important decomposers in cold climates.

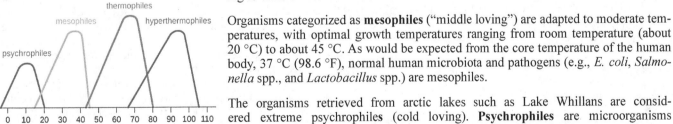

Figure 13 *The graph shows growth rate of bacteria as a function of temperature. Notice that the curves are skewed toward the optimum temperature. The skewing of the growth curve is thought to reflect the rapid denaturation of proteins as the temperature rises past the optimum for growth of the microorganism.*

Organisms that grow at optimum temperatures of 50 °C to a maximum of 80 °C are called **thermophiles** ("heat loving"). They do not multiply at room temperature. Thermophiles are widely distributed in hot springs, geothermal soils, and manmade environments such as garden compost piles where the microbes break down kitchen scraps and vegetal material. Examples of thermophiles include *Thermus aquaticus* and *Geobacillus* spp. Higher up on the extreme temperature scale we find the **hyperthermophiles**, which are characterized by growth ranges from 80 °C to a maximum of 110 °C, with some extreme examples that survive temperatures above 121 °C, the average temperature of an autoclave. The hydrothermal vents at the bottom of the ocean are a prime example of extreme environments, with temperatures reaching an estimated 340 °C. Microbes isolated from the vents achieve optimal growth at temperatures higher than 100 °C. Noteworthy examples are *Pyrobolus* and *Pyrodictium*, archaea that grow at 105 °C and survive autoclaving.

Figure 14 *A black smoker at the bottom of the ocean belches hot, chemical-rich water, and heats the surrounding waters. Sea vents provide an extreme environment that is nonetheless teeming with macroscopic life (the red tubeworms) supported by an abundant microbial ecosystem. (credit: NOAA)*

Osmotic Pressure

Most natural environments tend to have lower solute concentrations than the cytoplasm of most microorganisms. Rigid cell walls protect the cells from bursting in a dilute environment. Not much protection is available against high osmotic pressure (hypertonic solutions). In this case, water, following its concentration gradient, flows out of the cell. This results in plasmolysis (the shrinking of the protoplasm away from the intact cell wall) and cell death. This fact explains why brines and layering meat and fish in salt are time-honored methods of preserving food. Microorganisms called **halophiles** ("salt loving") actually require high salt concentrations for growth. These organisms are found in marine environments where salt concentrations hover at 3.5%. Extreme halophilic microorganisms, such as the red alga *Dunaliella salina* and the archaeal species *Halobacterium*, grow in hypersaline lakes such as the Great Salt Lake, which is 3.5–8 times saltier than the ocean, and the Dead Sea, which is 10 times saltier than the ocean.

Although most **facultative halophiles**, for example *Halomonas* spp. in salt marshes, do not need high concentrations of salt for growth, they will survive and divide in the presence of high salt. Not surprisingly, the staphylococci, micrococci, and corynebacteria that colonize our skin tolerate salt in their environment. Facultative halophiles that are pathogens are an important cause of food-borne illnesses because they survive and multiply in salty food. For example, the halotolerant bacteria *S. aureus*, *Bacillus cereus*, and *V. cholerae* produce dangerous enterotoxins and are major causes of food poisoning.

Figure 15 *Photograph taken from space of the Great Salt Lake in Utah. The purple color is caused by high density of the alga Dunaliella and the archaean Halobacterium spp. (credit: NASA)*

Decreasing the water content of foods by drying, as in jerky, or through freeze-drying or by increasing osmotic pressure, as in brine and jams, are common methods of preventing spoilage. In general, fungi can tolerate drier

The Viral Life Cycle

All viruses depend on their host cells for reproduction and metabolic processes. By themselves, viruses do not encode for all of the enzymes necessary for viral replication. But within a host cell, a virus can commandeer cellular machinery to produce more viral particles. Two of the ways viruses multiply in prokaryotic cells are through the lytic and lysogenic cycles. These are similar, but not identical, to the way viruses multiply in eukaryotic cells. Our understanding of the lytic and lysogenic cycles can provide an appreciation for viral infection in eukaryotes.

The Life Cycle of Viruses with Prokaryote Hosts

The life cycle of bacteriophages has been a good model for understanding how viruses affect the cells they infect, since similar processes have been observed for eukaryotic viruses, which can cause immediate death of the cell or establish a latent or chronic infection.

During the **lytic cycle** of phage, the bacteriophage takes over the cell, reproduces new phages, and destroys the cell. There are five stages in the bacteriophage lytic cycle. **Attachment** is the first stage in the infection process in which the phage interacts with specific bacterial surface receptors. Most phages have a narrow host range and may infect one species of bacteria or one strain within a species.

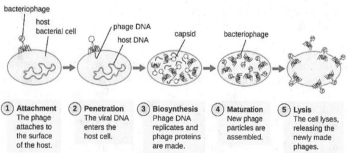

① **Attachment**	② **Penetration**	③ **Biosynthesis**	④ **Maturation**	⑤ **Lysis**
The phage attaches to the surface of the host.	The viral DNA enters the host cell.	Phage DNA replicates and phage proteins are made.	New phage particles are assembled.	The cell lyses, releasing the newly made phages.

Figure 16 *A virulent phage shows only the lytic cycle pictured here. In the lytic cycle, the phage replicates and lyses the host cell*

This unique recognition can be exploited for targeted treatment of bacterial infection by phage therapy or for phage typing to identify unique bacterial subspecies or strains. The second stage of infection is **entry** or **penetration**. This occurs through contraction of the tail sheath, which acts like a hypodermic needle to inject the viral genome through the cell wall and membrane. The phage head and remaining components remain outside the bacteria.

The third stage of infection is **biosynthesis** of new viral components. After entering the host cell, the virus synthesizes virus-encoded endonucleases to degrade the bacterial chromosome. It then hijacks the host cell to replicate, transcribe, and translate the necessary viral components (capsomeres, sheath, base plates, tail fibers, and viral enzymes) for the assembly of new viruses. During the **maturation (or assembly)** phase, new virions are created. The final stage is **release**. Mature viruses burst out of the host cell in a process called lysis and the progeny viruses are liberated into the environment to infect new cells.

In a **lysogenic cycle**, the phage genome also enters the cell through **attachment** and **penetration**. During the lysogenic cycle, instead of killing the host, the phage genome integrates into the bacterial chromosome and becomes part of the host. The integrated phage genome is called a **prophage**. As the bacterium replicates its chromosome, it also replicates the phage's DNA and passes it on to new daughter cells during reproduction. The presence of the phage may alter the phenotype of the bacterium, since it can bring in extra genes (e.g., toxin genes that can increase bacterial virulence). During lysogeny, the prophage will persist in the host chromosome until induction, which results in the excision of the viral genome from the host chromosome. After induction has occurred the phage can proceed through a lytic cycle and then undergo lysogeny in a newly infected cell.

Life Cycle of Viruses with Animal Hosts

Lytic animal viruses follow similar infection stages to bacteriophages: attachment, penetration, biosynthesis, maturation, and release. However, the mechanisms of penetration, nucleic-acid biosynthesis, and release differ between bacterial and animal viruses. Many viruses are host specific, meaning they only infect a certain type of host; and most viruses only infect certain types of cells within tissues. Examples of this are demonstrated by the poliovirus, which only infect the tissues of the brain and spinal cord, or the influenza virus, which has a primary attraction for the respiratory tract.

Persistent Infections

Many viral infections are considered **acute** meaning the virus infects cells, the host shows signs of illness then usually recovers over a relatively short time. **Persistent infection** occurs when a virus is not completely cleared from the system of the host but stays in certain tissues or organs of the infected person. The virus may remain silent or undergo productive infection without seriously harming or killing the host. Mechanisms of persistent infection may involve the regulation of the viral or host gene expressions or the alteration of the host immune response. The two primary categories of persistent infections are **latent infection** and **chronic infection**. Examples of viruses that cause latent infections include herpes simplex virus (oral and genital herpes), varicella-zoster virus (chickenpox and shingles), and Epstein-Barr virus (mononucleosis). Hepatitis C virus and HIV are two examples of viruses that cause long-term chronic infections.

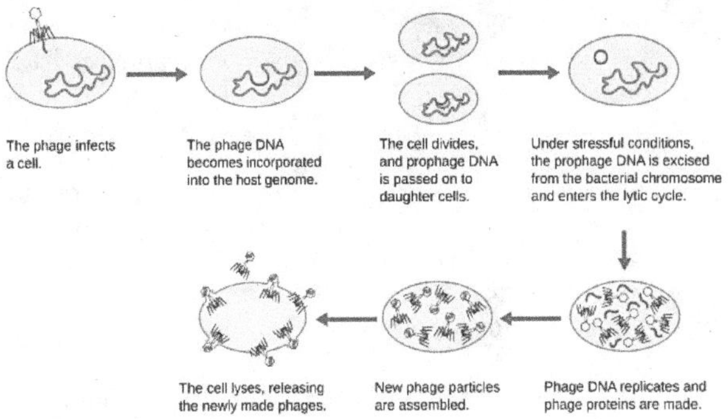

Not all animal viruses undergo replication by the lytic cycle. There are viruses that are capable of remaining hidden or dormant inside the cell in a process called **latency** (causing a **latent infection**). These types of viruses are known as latent viruses and may cause latent infections. Viruses capable of latency may initially cause an acute infection before becoming dormant.

For example, the varicella-zoster virus infects many cells throughout the body and causes chickenpox, characterized by a rash of blisters covering the skin. About 10 to 12 days postinfection, the disease resolves and the virus goes dormant, living within nerve-cell ganglia for years. During this time, the virus does not kill the nerve cells or continue replicating. It is not clear why the virus stops replicating within the nerve cells and expresses few viral proteins but, in some cases, typically after many years of dormancy, the virus is reactivated and causes a new disease called shingles. Whereas chickenpox affects many areas throughout the body, shingles is a nerve cell-specific disease emerging from the ganglia in which the virus was dormant.

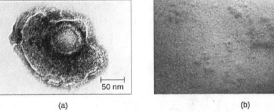

The phage infects a cell.

The phage DNA becomes incorporated into the host genome.

The cell divides, and prophage DNA is passed on to daughter cells.

Under stressful conditions, the prophage DNA is excised from the bacterial chromosome and enters the lytic cycle.

The cell lyses, releasing the newly made phages.

New phage particles are assembled.

Phage DNA replicates and phage proteins are made.

Figure 17 *A temperate bacteriophage has both lytic and lysogenic cycles. In the lysogenic cycle, phage DNA is incorporated into the host genome, forming a prophage, which is passed on to subsequent generations of cells. Environmental stressors such as starvation or exposure to toxic chemicals may cause the prophage to be excised and enter the lytic cycle.*

Latent viruses may remain dormant by existing as circular viral genome molecules outside of the host chromosome. Others become proviruses by integrating into the host genome. During dormancy, viruses do not cause any symptoms of disease and may be difficult to detect. A patient may be unaware that he or she is carrying the virus unless a viral diagnostic test has been performed.

A **chronic infection** is a disease with symptoms that are recurrent or persistent over a long time. Some viral infections can be chronic if the body is unable to eliminate the virus. HIV is an example of a virus that produces a chronic infection, often after a long period of latency. Once a person becomes infected with HIV, the virus can be detected in tissues continuously thereafter, but untreated patients often experience no symptoms for years. However, the virus maintains chronic persistence through several mechanisms that interfere with immune function, including preventing expression of viral antigens on the surface of infected cells, altering immune cells themselves, restricting expression of viral genes, and rapidly changing viral antigens through mutation. Eventually, the damage to the immune system results in progression of the disease leading to acquired immunodeficiency syndrome (AIDS). The various mechanisms that HIV uses to avoid being cleared by the immune system are also used by other chronically infecting viruses, including the hepatitis C virus.

50 nm

(a)

(b)

Figure 18 *(a) Varicella-zoster, the virus that causes chickenpox, has an enveloped icosahedral capsid visible in this transmission electron micrograph. Its double-stranded DNA genome becomes incorporated in the host DNA. (b) After a period of latency, the virus can reactivate in the form of shingles, usually manifesting as a painful, localized rash on one side of the body. (credit a: modification of work by Erskine Palmer and B.G. Partin—scale-bar data from Matt Russell; credit b: modification of work by Rosmarie Voegtli)*

Oral Herpes

A common skin virus is **herpes simplex virus (HSV)**. HSV has historically been divided into two types, **HSV-1** and **HSV-2**. HSV-1 is typically transmitted by direct oral contact between individuals, and is usually associated with oral herpes. HSV-2 is usually transmitted sexually and is typically associated with genital herpes. However, both HSV-1 and HSV-2 are capable of infecting any mucous membrane, and the incidence of genital HSV-1 and oral HSV-2 infections has been increasing in recent years.

Infection by HSV-1 commonly manifests as cold sores or fever blisters, usually on or around the lips. HSV-1 is highly contagious, with some studies suggesting that up to 65% of the US population is infected; however, many infected individuals are asymptomatic. Moreover, the virus can be latent for long periods, residing in the trigeminal nerve ganglia between recurring bouts of symptoms. Recurrence can be triggered by stress or environmental conditions (systemic or affecting the skin). When lesions are present, they may blister, break open, and crust. The virus can be spread through direct contact, even when a patient is asymptomatic.

While the lips, mouth, and face are the most common sites for HSV-1 infections, lesions can spread to other areas of the body. Wrestlers and other athletes involved in contact sports may develop lesions on the neck, shoulders, and trunk. This condition is often called herpes gladiatorum. Herpes lesions that develop on the fingers are often called herpetic whitlow.

Chickenpox and Shingles

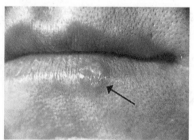

Figure 19 *This cold sore was caused by HSV-1. (credit: Centers for Disease Control and Prevention)*

Chickenpox, also known as varicella, was once a common viral childhood disease. The causative agent of chickenpox, the varicella-zoster virus, is a member of the herpesvirus family. In children, the disease is mild and self-limiting, and is easily transmitted by direct contact or inhalation of material from the skin lesions. In adults, however, chickenpox infections can be much more severe and can lead to pneumonia and birth defects in the case of infected pregnant women.

Once infected, most individuals acquire a lifetime immunity to future chickenpox outbreaks. For this reason, parents once held "chickenpox parties" for their children. At these events, uninfected children were intentionally exposed to an infected individual so they would contract the disease earlier in life, when the incidence of complications is very low, rather than risk a more severe infection later.

After the initial viral exposure, chickenpox has an incubation period of about 2 weeks. The initial infection of the respiratory tract leads to viremia and eventually produces fever and chills. A pustular rash then develops on the face, progresses to the trunk, and then the extremities, although most form on the trunk. Eventually, the lesions burst and form a crusty scab. Individuals with chickenpox are infectious from about 2 days before the outbreak of the rash until all the lesions have scabbed over.

Like other herpesviruses, the varicella-zoster virus can become dormant in nerve cells. While the pustular vesicles are developing, the virus moves along sensory nerves to the dorsal ganglia in the spinal cord. Once there, the varicella-zoster virus can remain latent for decades. These dormant viruses may be reactivated later in life by a variety of stimuli, including stress, aging, and immunosuppression. Once reactivated, the virus moves along sensory nerves to the skin of the face or trunk. This results in the production of the painful lesions

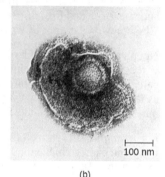

Figure 18 *(a) Varicella-zoster, the virus that causes chickenpox, has an enveloped icosahedral capsid visible in this transmission electron micrograph. Its double-stranded DNA genome becomes incorporated in the host DNA. (b) After a period of latency, the virus can reactivate in the form of shingles, usually manifesting as a painful, localized rash on one side of the body. (credit a: modification of work by Erskine Palmer and B.G. Partin—scale-bar data from Matt Russell; credit b: modification of work by Rosmarie Voegtli)*

in a condition known as **shingles**. These symptoms generally last for 2–6 weeks, and may recur more than once. Postherpetic neuralgia, pain signals sent from damaged nerves long after the other symptoms have subsided, is also possible. In addition, the virus can spread to other organs in immunocompromised individuals. A person with shingles lesions can transmit the virus to a nonimmune contact, and the newly infected individual would develop chickenpox as the primary infection. Shingles cannot be transmitted from one person to another.

The primary diagnosis of chickenpox in children is mainly based on the presentation of a pustular rash of the trunk. Treatment for chickenpox infections in children is usually not required. In patients with shingles, acyclovir treatment can often reduce the severity and length of symptoms, and diminish the risk of postherpetic neuralgia. An effective vaccine is now available for chickenpox. A vaccine is also available for adults older than 60 years who were infected with chickenpox in their youth. This vaccine reduces the likelihood of a shingles outbreak by boosting the immune

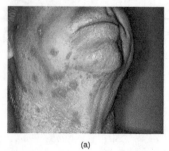

Figure 21 *(a) An individual suffering from shingles. (b) The rash is formed because of the reactivation of a varicella-zoster infection that was initially contracted in childhood. (credit a: modification of work by National Institute of Allergy and Infectious Diseases (NIAID); credit b: modification of work by Centers for Disease Control and Prevention)*

defenses that are keeping the latent infection in check and preventing reactivation.

Cultivation of Viruses

Unlike bacteria, many of which can be grown on an artificial nutrient medium, viruses require a living host cell for replication. Infected host cells (eukaryotic or prokaryotic) can be cultured and grown, and then the growth medium can be harvested as a source of virus. Three common ways for the cultivation of viruses is in **living organisms** (such as bacteria, plants, animals), in **cell cultures** specific to the virus, and in **fertilized chicken eggs**. Bacteriophages can be grown in the presence of a dense layer of bacteria (also called a bacterial lawn) grown in a 0.7 % soft agar in a Petri dish or flat (horizontal) flask. For lytic bacteriophages, lysing of the bacterial hosts can then be readily observed when a clear zone called a **plaque** is detected. As the phage kills the bacteria, many plaques are observed among the cloudy bacterial lawn.

Animal viruses require cells within a host animal or tissue-culture cells derived from an animal. Animal virus cultivation is important for 1) identification and diagnosis of pathogenic viruses in clinical specimens, 2) production of vaccines, and 3) basic research studies. In vivo host sources can be a developing embryo in an embryonated bird's egg (e.g., chicken, turkey) or a whole animal. For example, most of the influenza vaccine manufactured for annual flu vaccination programs is cultured in hens' eggs.

The embryo or host animal serves as an incubator for viral replication. Location within the embryo or host animal is important. Many viruses must be introduced into a specific site for growth. Within an embryo, target sites include the amniotic cavity, the chorioallantoic membrane, or the yolk sac. Viral infection may damage tissue membranes, producing lesions called pox; disrupt embryonic development; or cause the death of the embryo.

For in vitro studies, various types of cells can be used to support the growth of viruses. A primary cell culture is freshly prepared from animal organs or tissues. Cells are extracted from tissues by mechanical scraping or mincing to release cells or by an enzymatic method using trypsin or collagenase to break up tissue and release single cells into suspension. Because of anchorage-

(a)   (b)

Figure 22 (a) Flasks like this may be used to culture human or animal cells for viral culturing. (b) These plates contain bacteriophage T4 grown on an Escherichia coli lawn. Clear plaques are visible where host bacterial cells have been lysed. Viral titers increase on the plates to the left. (credit a: modification of work by National Institutes of Health; credit b: modification of work by American Society for Microbiology)

 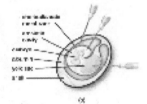

Figure 23 (a) The cells within chicken eggs are used to culture different types of viruses. (b) Viruses can be replicated in various locations within the egg, including the chorioallantoic membrane, the amniotic cavity, and the yolk sac. (credit a: modification of work by "Chung Hoang"/ YouTube)

Microbial Genetics

Central Dogma

Figure 1 *Escherichia coli (left) may not appear to have much in common with an elephant (right), but the genetic blueprints for these vastly different organisms are both encoded in DNA. (credit left: modification of work by NIAID; credit right: modification of work by Tom Lubbock)*

In 1954, French scientist and future Nobel laureate **Jacques** Monod (1910–1976) famously said, "What is true in *E. coli* is true in the elephant," suggesting that the biochemistry of life was maintained throughout evolution and is shared in all forms of known life. Since Monod's famous statement, we have learned a great deal about the mechanisms of gene regulation, expression, and replication in living cells. All cells use DNA for information storage, share the same genetic code, and use similar mechanisms to replicate and express it. Although many aspects of genetics are universally shared, variations do exist among contemporary genetic systems. We now know that within the shared overall theme of the genetic mechanism, there are significant differences among living cells.

DNA serves two essential functions that deal with cellular information. First, DNA is the genetic material responsible for inheritance and is passed from parent to offspring for all life on earth. To preserve the integrity of this genetic information, DNA must be replicated with great accuracy, with minimal errors that introduce changes to the DNA sequence. A **genome**, contains the full complement of DNA within a cell and is organized into smaller, discrete units called genes that are arranged on chromosomes and plasmids. The second function of DNA is to direct and regulate the construction of the proteins necessary to a cell for growth and reproduction in a particular cellular environment.

A **gene** is composed of DNA that is "read" or transcribed to produce an RNA molecule during the process of transcription. One major type of RNA molecule, called messenger RNA (mRNA), provides the information for the ribosome to catalyze protein synthesis in a process called translation. The processes of transcription and translation are collectively referred to as **gene expression**. Gene expression is the synthesis of a specific protein with a sequence of amino acids that is encoded in the gene. The flow of genetic information from DNA to RNA to protein is described by the **central dogma**.

A cell's genotype is the full collection of genes it contains, whereas its phenotype is the set of observable characteristics that result from those genes. The phenotype is the product of the array of proteins being produced by the cell at a given time, which is influenced by the cell's genotype as well as interactions with the cell's environment. Genes code for proteins that have functions in the cell.

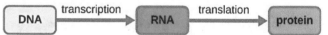

Figure 2 *The central dogma states that DNA encodes messenger RNA, which, in turn, encodes protein.*

Viral genomes are relatively small compared to those of cellular organisms. Since viruses must live in a host cell, they use many proteins made by the host cell and do not need their own genes to encode for those proteins. Some viruses, like those that cause influenza, have a genome composed of RNA rather than DNA. RNA is inherently a less stable molecule than DNA making RNA viruses more prone to genetic changes than microorganisms with a genome composed of DNA.

Mutations

A **mutation** is a heritable change in the DNA sequence of an organism or, in the case of RNA viruses, a change in the RNA sequence. The resulting organism, called a mutant, may have a recognizable change in phenotype compared to the wild type, which is the phenotype most commonly observed in nature. A change in the DNA sequence is conferred to mRNA through transcription, and may lead to an altered amino acid sequence in a protein on translation. Because proteins carry out the vast majority of cellular functions, a change in amino acid sequence in a protein may lead to an altered phenotype for the cell and organism.

Effects of Mutations on Protein Structure and Function

Mutations may have a wide range of effects on protein function. A mutation will sometimes result in the same amino acid being incorporated into the resulting polypeptide despite the sequence change. This change would have no effect on the protein's structure. Some mutations result in a different amino acid being incorporated into the resulting polypeptide. The effect of the mutation depends on how chemically different the new amino acid is from the wild-type amino acid. The location of the changed amino acid within the protein also is important. For example, if the changed amino acid is part of the enzyme's active site, then the effect of the mutation may be significant. Many of these mutations result in proteins that are still functional, at least to some degree. Rarely, a mutation may be beneficial. Under the right environmental conditions, this type of mutation may give the organism that harbors it a selective advantage. Mutations result in the synthesis of proteins that are shorter than the wild type and typically not functional.

Causes of Mutations

Mistakes in the process of DNA replication can cause mutations to occur. The error rate of DNA polymerase is one incorrect base per billion base pairs replicated. Exposure to **mutagens** can also cause mutations, which are various types of chemical agents or radiation. Exposure to a mutagen can increase the rate of mutation more than 1000-fold. Mutagens are often also carcinogens, agents that cause cancer. However, whereas nearly all carcinogens are mutagenic, not all mutagens are necessarily carcinogens.

Horizontal Gene Transfer

Typically, when we consider genetic transfer, we think of **vertical gene transfer**, the transmission of genetic information from genera- tion to generation. Vertical gene transfer is by far the main mode of transmission of genetic information in all cells. Genetic diversity is also introduced during sexual reproduction, when the genetic information from two parents, each with different complements of genetic information, are combined, producing new combinations of parental genotypes in the diploid offspring. The occurrence of mutations also contributes to genetic diversity in a population. Genetic diversity of offspring is useful in changing or inconsistent environments and may be one reason for the evolutionary success of sexual reproduction.

When prokaryotes and eukaryotes reproduce asexually, they transfer a nearly identical copy of their genetic material to their offspring through vertical gene transfer. Although asexual reproduction produces more offspring more quickly, any benefits of diversity among those offspring are lost. How then do organisms whose dominant reproductive mode is asexual create genetic diversity? In prokaryotes, **horizontal gene transfer (HGT),** the introduction of genetic material from one organism to another organism within the same gen- eration, is an important way to introduce genetic diversity. HGT allows even distantly related species to share genes, influencing their phenotypes. It is thought that HGT is more prevalent in prokaryotes but that only a small fraction of the prokaryotic genome may be transferred by this type of transfer at any one time. As the phenomenon is investigated more thoroughly, it may be revealed to be even more common. Many scientists believe that HGT and mutation are significant sources of genetic variation, the raw material for the pro- cess of natural selection, in prokaryotes. Although HGT is more common among evolutionarily related organisms, it may occur between any two species that live together in a natural community.

HGT in prokaryotes is known to occur by the three primary mechanisms that are illustrated in the figure:

1. Transformation: naked DNA is taken up from the environment

2. Transduction: genes are transferred between cells in a virus

3. Conjugation: use of a hollow tube called a conjugation pilus to transfer genes between cells

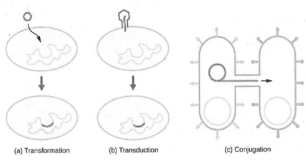

(a) Transformation   (b) Transduction   (c) Conjugation

Figure 3 *There are three prokaryote-specific mechanisms lead- ing to horizontal gene transfer in prokaryotes. a) In transforma- tion, the cell takes up DNA directly from the environment. The DNA may remain separate as a plasmid or be incorporated into the host genome. b) In transduction, a bacteriophage injects DNA that is a hybrid of viral DNA and DNA from a previously infected bacterial cell. c) In conjugation, DNA is transferred between cells through a cytoplasmic bridge after a conjugation pilus draws the two cells close enough to form the bridge.*

Antigenic Variation in Viruses

Antigenic variation also occurs in certain types of enveloped viruses, including influenza viruses, which exhibit two forms of antigenic variation: **antigenic drift** and **antigenic shift** . Anti- genic drift is the result of mutations causing slight changes in the spike proteins hemagglutinin (H) and neuraminidase (N). On the other hand, antigenic shift is a major change in spike proteins due to gene reassortment. This reassortment for anti- genic shift occurs typically when two different influenza virus- es infect the same host.

The rate of antigenic variation in influenza viruses is very high, making it difficult for the immune system to recognize the many different strains of Influenzavirus. Although the body may de- velop immunity to one strain through natural exposure or vac- cination, antigenic variation results in the continual emergence of new strains that the immune system will not recognize. This is the main reason that vaccines against Influenzavirus must be given annually. Each year's influenza vaccine provides protec- tion against the most prevalent strains for that year, but new or different strains may be more prevalent the following year.

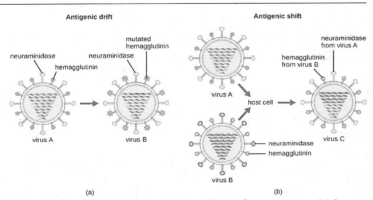

Figure 4 *Antigenic drift and antigenic shift in influenza viruses. (a) In anti- genic drift, mutations in the genes for the surface proteins neuraminidase and/ or hemagglutinin result in small antigenic changes over time. (b) In antigenic shift, simultaneous infection of a cell with two different influenza viruses re- sults in mixing of the genes. The resultant virus possesses a mixture of the proteins of the original viruses. Influenza pandemics can often be traced to antigenic shifts*

Influenza

Commonly known as the flu, **influenza** is a common viral disease of the lower respiratory system caused by an orthomyxovirus. Influ- enza is pervasive worldwide and causes 3,000–50,000 deaths each year in the United States. The annual mortality rate can vary greatly depending on the virulence of the strain(s) responsible for seasonal epidemics.

Influenza infections are most typically characterized by fever, chills, and body aches. This is followed by symptoms similar to the common cold that may last a week or more. The table compares the signs and symptoms of influenza and the common cold.

Comparing the Common Cold and Influenza		
Sign/Symptom	Common Cold	Influenza
Fever	Low (37.2 °C [99 °F])	High (39 °C [102.2 °F])
Headache	Common	Common
Aches and pains	Mild	Severe
Fatigue	Slight	Severe
Nasal congestion	Common	Rare
Sneezing	Common	Rare

Table 2

In general, influenza is self-limiting. However, serious cases can lead to pneumonia and other complications that can be fatal. Such cases are more common in the very young and the elderly; however, certain strains of influenza virus (like the 1918–1919 variant discussed later in this chapter) are more lethal to young adults than to the very young or old. Strains that affect young adults are believed to involve a cytokine storm—a positive feedback loop that forms between cytokine production and leukocytes. This cytokine storm produces an acute inflammatory response that leads to rapid fluid accumulation in the lungs, culminating in pulmonary failure. In such cases, the ability to mount a vigorous immune response is actually detrimental to the patient. The very young and very old are less susceptible to this effect because their immune systems are less robust.

The influenza virus is primarily transmitted by direct contact and inhalation of aerosols.

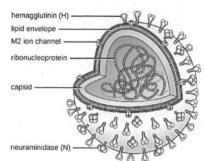

Figure 5 *The illustration shows the structure of an influenza virus. The viral envelope is studded with copies of the proteins neuraminidase and hemagglutinin, and surrounds the individual seven or eight RNA genome segments. (credit: modification of work by Dan Higgins, Centers for Disease Control and Prevention)*

There are three genetically related influenza viruses, called A, B, and C. The influenza A viruses have different subtypes based on the structure of their hemagglutinin and neuraminidase proteins. There are currently 18 known subtypes of hemagglutinin and 11 known subtypes of neuraminidase. Influenza viruses are serologically characterized by the type of H and N proteins that they possess. Of the nearly 200 different combinations of H and N, only a few, such as the H1N1 strain, are associated with human disease. The influenza viruses A, B, and C make up three of the five major groups of orthomyxoviruses. The differences between the three types of influenza are summarized in the table. The most virulent group is the influenza A viruses, which cause seasonal pandemics of influenza each year. Influenza A virus can infect a variety of animals, including pigs, horses, pigs, and even whales and dolphins. Influenza B virus is less virulent and is sometimes associated with epidemic outbreaks. Influenza C virus generally produces the mildest disease symptoms and is rarely connected with epidemics. Neither influenza B virus nor influenza C virus has significant animal reservoirs.

The Three Major Groups of Influenza Viruses			
	Influenza A virus	Influenza B virus	Influenza C virus
Severity	Severe	Moderate	Mild
Animal reservoir	Yes	No	No
Genome segments	8	8	7
Population spread	Epidemic and pandemic	Epidemic	Sporadic
Antigenic variation	Shift/drift	Drift	Drift

Table 3

The most lethal influenza pandemic in recorded history occurred from 1918 through 1919. Near the end of World War I, an antigenic shift involving the recombination of avian and human viruses is thought to have produced a new H1N1 virus. This strain rapidly spread worldwide and is commonly claimed to have killed as many as 40 million to 50 million people—more than double the number killed in the war. Although referred to as the Spanish flu, this disease is thought to have originated in the United States. Regardless of its source, the conditions of World War I greatly contributed to the spread of this disease. Crowding, poor sanitation, and rapid mobilization of large numbers of personnel and animals facilitated the dissemination of the new virus once it appeared.

Several of the most important influenza pandemics of modern times have been associated with antigenic shifts. A few of these are summarized in the table.

Historical Influenza Outbreaks			
Years	Common Name	Serotype	Estimated Number of Deaths
1918–1919	Spanish flu	H1N1	20,000,000–40,000,000
1957–1958	Asian flu	N2N2	1,000,000–2,000,000
1968–1969	Hong Kong flu	H3N2	1,000,000–3,000,000
2009–2010	Swine flu	H1N1/09	152,000–575,000

Table 4

Genetic Methods for Classification and Identification of Microorganisms

Classification is the practice of organizing organisms into different groups based on their shared characteristics. Assigning prokaryotes to a certain species is challenging. They do not reproduce sexually, so it is not possible to classify them according to the presence or absence of interbreeding. Also, they do not have many morphological features. Traditionally, the classification of prokaryotes was based on their shape, staining patterns, and biochemical or physiological differences. More recently, as technology has improved, the nucleotide sequences in genes have become an important criterion of microbial classification.

Figure 6 Swedish botanist, zoologist, and physician Carolus Linnaeus developed a new system for categorizing plants and animals. In this 1853 portrait by Hendrik Hollander, Linnaeus is holding a twinflower, named Linnaea borealis in his honor.

Taxonomy is the science of classification. The most famous early taxonomist was a Swedish botanist, zoologist, and physician named Carolus Linnaeus (1701–1778). In 1735, Linnaeus published *Systema Naturae*, an 11-page booklet in which he proposed the Linnaean taxonomy, a system of categorizing and naming organisms using a standard format so scientists could discuss organisms using consistent terminology. He continued to revise and add to the book, which grew into multiple volumes.

In his taxonomy, Linnaeus divided the natural world into three kingdoms: animal, plant, and mineral (the mineral kingdom was later abandoned). Within the animal and plant kingdoms, he grouped organisms using a hierarchy of increasingly specific levels and sublevels based on their similarities. The names of the levels in Linnaeus's original taxonomy were kingdom, class, order, family, genus (plural: genera), and species. Species was, and continues to be, the most specific and basic taxonomic unit. With advances in technology, other scientists gradually made refinements to the Linnaean system and eventually created new systems for classifying organisms. In the 1800s, there was a growing interest in developing taxonomies that took into account the evolutionary relationships, or phylogenies, of all different species of organisms on earth. One way to depict these relationships is via a diagram called a phylogenetic tree (or tree of life). In these diagrams, groups of organisms are arranged by how closely related they are thought to be. In early phylogenetic trees, the relatedness of organisms was inferred by their visible similarities, such as the presence or absence of hair or the number of limbs. Now, the analysis is more complicated. Today, phylogenic analyses include genetic, biochemical, and embryological comparisons.

Linnaeus's tree of life contained just two main branches for all living things: the animal and plant kingdoms. In 1866, Ernst Haeckel, a German biologist, philosopher, and physician, proposed another kingdom, Protista, for unicellular organisms. He later proposed a fourth kingdom, Monera, for unicellular organisms whose cells lack nuclei, like bacteria.

Nearly 100 years later, in 1969, American ecologist Robert Whittaker (1920–1980) proposed adding another kingdom—Fungi—in his tree of life. Whittaker's tree also contained a level of categorization above the kingdom level—the empire or superkingdom level—to distinguish between organisms that have membrane-bound nuclei in their cells (eukaryotes) and those that do not (prokaryotes). The figure shows how the tree of life has changed over time. Note that viruses are not found in any of these trees. That is because they are not made up of cells and thus it is difficult to determine where they would fit into a tree of life.

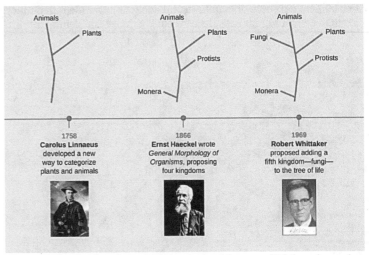

Figure 7 This timeline shows how the shape of the tree of life has changed over the centuries. Even today, the taxonomy of living organisms is continually being reevaluated and refined with advances in technology.

Haeckel's and Whittaker's trees presented hypotheses about the phylogeny of different organisms based on readily observable characteristics. But the advent of molecular genetics in the late 20th century revealed other ways to organize phylogenetic trees. Genetic methods allow for a standardized way to compare all living organisms without relying on observable characteristics that can often be subjective. Modern taxonomy relies heavily on comparing the nucleic acids (deoxyribonucleic acid [DNA] or ribonucleic acid [RNA]) or proteins from different organisms. The more similar the nucleic acids and proteins are between two organisms, the more closely related they are considered to be.

In the 1970s, American microbiologist Carl Woese discovered what appeared to be a "living record" of the evolution of organisms. He and his collaborator George Fox created a genetics-based tree of life based on similarities and differences they observed in the gene sequences coding for small subunit **ribosomal RNA (rRNA)** of different organisms. In the process, they discovered that a certain type of bacteria called archaea, were significantly different from other bacteria and eukaryotes in terms of their small subunit rRNA gene sequences. To accommodate this difference, they created a tree with **three Domains** above the level of Kingdom: **Archaea, Bacteria**, and **Eukarya** . Analysis of small subunit rRNA gene sequences suggests archaea, bacteria, and eukaryotes all evolved from a common ancestral cell type. The tree is skewed to show a closer evolutionary relationship between Archaea and Eukarya than they have to Bacteria.

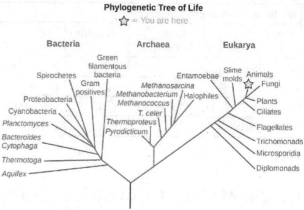

Figure 8 *Woese and Fox's phylogenetic tree contains three domains: Bacteria, Archaea, and Eukarya. Domains Archaea and Bacteria contain all prokaryotic organisms, and Eukarya contains all eukaryotic organisms. (credit: modification of work by Eric Gaba)*

Classification and Taxonomy of Viruses

Although viruses are not classified in the three domains of life, their numbers are great enough to require classification. Since 1971, the International Union of Microbiological Societies Virology Division has given the task of developing, refining, and maintaining a universal virus taxonomy to the International Committee on Taxonomy of Viruses (ICTV). Since viruses can mutate so quickly, it can be difficult to classify them into a genus and a species epithet using the binomial nomenclature system. Thus, the ICTV's viral nomenclature system classifies viruses into families and genera based on viral genetics, chemistry, morphology, and mechanism of multiplication. To date, the ICTV has classified known viruses in seven orders, 96 families, and 350 genera. Viral family names end in -*viridae* (e.g, *Parvoviridae*) and genus names end in −*virus* (e.g., *Parvovirus*).

Aside from formal systems of nomenclature, viruses are often informally grouped into categories based on chemistry, morphology, or other characteristics they share in common. Categories may include naked or enveloped structure, single-stranded (ss) or double-stranded (ds) DNA or ss or ds RNA genomes, segmented or nonsegmented genomes, and positive-strand (+) or negative-strand (−) RNA. For example, herpes viruses can be classified as a dsDNA enveloped virus; human immunodeficiency virus (HIV) is a +ssRNA enveloped virus, and tobacco mosaic virus is a +ssRNA virus. Other characteristics such as host specificity, tissue specificity, capsid shape, and special genes or enzymes may also be used to describe groups of similar viruses.

Genetic Methods for Identification of Microorganisms

The techniques used for the analysis of rRNA sequences to classify microorganisms can also be applied to the identification of microorganisms. In the study of **metagenomics**, genetic material from environmental samples is analyzed resulting in the identification of almost all the microorganisms present in the sample. Currently, there about 7,000 species of bacteria that have been cultured in laboratories and described. It is predicted that this is just a small fraction of the bacterial species actually present in a given environment.

For clinical purposes, it is important that bacteria are identified quickly and inexpensively and therefore biochemical tests are still used extensively. For organisms that present challenges in identification, more advanced techniques for genetic analysis are sometimes used.

Common Pathogenic Viruses			
Genome	Family	Example Virus	Clinical Features
dsDNA, enveloped	*Poxviridae*	*Orthopoxvirus*	Skin papules, pustules, lesions
	Poxviridae	*Parapoxvirus*	Skin lesions
	Herpesviridae	*Simplexvirus*	Cold sores, genital herpes, sexually transmitted disease
dsDNA, naked	*Adenoviridae*	*Atadenovirus*	Respiratory infection (common cold)
	Papillomaviridae	*Papillomavirus*	Genital warts, cervical, vulvar, or vaginal cancer
	Reoviridae	*Reovirus*	Gastroenteritis severe diarrhea (stomach flu)
ssDNA, naked	*Parvoviridae*	*Adeno-associated dependoparvovirus A*	Respiratory tract infection
	Parvoviridae	*Adeno-associated dependoparvovirus B*	Respiratory tract infection
dsRNA, naked	*Reoviridae*	*Rotavirus*	Gastroenteritis
+ssRNA, naked	*Picornaviridae*	*Enterovirus C*	Poliomyelitis
	Picornaviridae	*Rhinovirus*	Upper respiratory tract infection (common cold)
	Picornaviridae	*Hepatovirus*	Hepatitis
+ssRNA, enveloped	*Togaviridae*	*Alphavirus*	Encephalitis, hemorrhagic fever
	Togaviridae	*Rubivirus*	Rubella
	Retroviridae	*Lentivirus*	Acquired immune deficiency syndrome (AIDS)
−ssRNA, enveloped	*Filoviridae*	*Zaire Ebolavirus*	Hemorrhagic fever
	Orthomyxoviridae	*Influenzavirus A, B, C*	Flu
	Rhabdoviridae	*Lyssavirus*	Rabies

Control of Microbial Growth

Location	Average number CFUs per 6.5 × 6.5 cm area
Door latch	256
Door lock	14
Door lock control	182
Door handle	29
Window control	4
Cruise control button	69
Steering wheel	239
Interior steering wheel	390
Radio volume knob	99
Gear shifter	115
Center console	506

Figure 1 *Most environments, including cars, are not sterile. A study[1] analyzed 11 locations within 18 different cars to determine the number of microbial colony-forming units (CFUs) present. The center console harbored by far the most microbes (506 CFUs), possibly because that is where drinks are placed (and often spilled). Frequently touched sites also had high concentrations. (credit "photo": modification of work by Jeff Wilcox)*

How clean is clean? People wash their cars and vacuum the carpets, but most would not want to eat from these surfaces. Similarly, we might eat with silverware cleaned in a dishwasher, but we could not use the same dishwasher to clean surgical instruments. As these examples illustrate, "clean" is a relative term. Car washing, vacuuming, and dishwashing all reduce the microbial load on the items treated, thus making them "cleaner." But whether they are "clean enough" depends on their intended use. Because people do not normally eat from cars or carpets, these items do not require the same level of cleanliness that silverware does. Likewise, because silverware is not used for invasive surgery, these utensils do not require the same level of cleanliness as surgical equipment, which requires sterilization to prevent infection.

Why not play it safe and sterilize everything? Sterilizing everything we come in contact with is impractical, as well as potentially dangerous. As this chapter will demonstrate, sterilization protocols often require time- and labor-intensive treatments that may degrade the quality of the item being treated or have toxic effects on users. Therefore, the user must consider the item's intended application when choosing a cleaning method to ensure that it is "clean enough."

The Germ Theory of Disease

Prior to the discovery of microbes during the 17th century, other theories circulated about the origins of disease. For example, the ancient Greeks proposed the **miasma theory**, which held that disease originated from particles emanating from decomposing matter, such as that in sewage or cesspits. Such particles infected humans in close proximity to the rotting material. Diseases including the Black Death, which ravaged Europe's population during the Middle Ages, were thought to have originated in this way.In 1546, Italian physician Girolamo Fracastoro proposed, in his essay *De Contagione et Contagiosis Morbis*, that seed-like spores may be transferred between individuals through direct contact, exposure to contaminated clothing, or through the air. We now recognize Fracastoro as an early proponent of the **germ theory of disease**, which states that diseases may result from microbial infection. However, in the 16th century, Fracastoro's ideas were not widely accepted and would be largely forgotten until the 19th century.

In 1847, Hungarian obstetrician **Ignaz Semmelweis** observed that mothers who gave birth in hospital wards staffed by physicians and medical students were more likely to suffer and die from puerperal fever after childbirth (10%–20% mortality rate) than were mothers in wards staffed by midwives (1% mortality rate). Semmelweis observed medical students performing autopsies and then subsequently carrying out vaginal examinations on living patients without washing their hands in between. He suspected that the students carried disease from the autopsies to the patients they examined. His suspicions were supported by the untimely death of a friend, a physician who contracted a fatal wound infection after a postmortem examination of a woman who had died of a puerperal infection. The dead physician's wound had been caused by a scalpel used during the examination, and his subsequent illness and death closely paralleled that of the dead patient.

Although Semmelweis did not know the true cause of puerperal fever, he proposed that physicians were somehow transferring the causative agent to their patients. He suggested that the number of puerperal fever cases could be reduced if physicians and medical students simply washed their hands with chlorinated lime water before and after examining every patient. When this practice was implemented, the maternal mortality rate in mothers cared for by physicians dropped to the same 1% mortality rate observed among mothers cared for by midwives. This demonstrated that handwashing was a very effective method for preventing disease transmission. Despite this great success, many discounted Semmelweis's work at the time, and physicians were slow to adopt the simple procedure of handwashing to prevent infections in their patients because it contradicted established norms for that time period.

Around the same time Semmelweis was promoting handwashing, in 1848, British physician John Snow conducted studies to track the source of cholera outbreaks in London. By tracing the outbreaks to two specific water sources, both of which were contaminated by sewage, Snow ultimately demonstrated that cholera bacteria were transmitted via drinking water. Snow's work is influential in that it represents the first known epidemiological study, and it resulted in the first known public health response to an epidemic. The work of both Semmelweis and Snow clearly refuted the prevailing miasma theory of the day, showing that disease is not only transmitted through the air but also through contaminated items.

Although the work of Semmelweis and Snow successfully showed the role of sanitation in preventing infectious disease, the cause of disease was not fully understood. The subsequent work of **Louis Pasteur**, **Robert Koch**, and **Joseph Lister** would further substantiate the germ theory of disease.

While studying the causes of beer and wine spoilage in 1856, Pasteur discovered properties of fermentation by microorganisms. He had demonstrated with his swan-neck flask experiments that airborne microbes, not spontaneous generation, were the cause of food spoilage, and he suggested that if microbes were responsible for food spoilage and fermentation, they could also be responsible for causing infection. This was the foundation for the germ theory of disease.

Meanwhile, British surgeon Joseph Lister was trying to determine the causes of postsurgical infections. Many physicians did not give credence to the idea that microbes on their hands, on their clothes, or in the air could infect patients' surgical wounds, despite the fact that 50% of surgical patients, on average, were dying of postsurgical infections.[15] Lister, however, was familiar with the work of Semmelweis and Pasteur; therefore, he insisted on handwashing and extreme cleanliness during surgery. In 1867, to further decrease the incidence of postsurgical wound infections, Lister began using carbolic acid (phenol) spray disinfectant/antiseptic during surgery. His extremely successful efforts to reduce postsurgical infection caused his techniques to become a standard medical practice.

Figure 2 *Ignaz Semmelweis (1818–1865) was a proponent of the importance of handwashing to prevent transfer of disease between patients by physicians.*

A few years later, Robert Koch proposed a series of postulates (Koch's postulates) based on the idea that the cause of a specific disease could be attributed to a specific microbe. Using these postulates, Koch and his colleagues were able to definitively identify the causative pathogens of specific diseases, including anthrax, tuberculosis, and cholera. Koch's "one microbe, one disease" concept was the culmination of the 19th century's paradigm shift away from miasma theory and toward the germ theory of disease.

(a) (b)

Figure 3 *Joseph Lister developed procedures for the proper care of surgical wounds and the sterilization of surgical equipment. (b) Robert Koch established a protocol to determine the cause of infectious disease. Both scientists contributed significantly to the acceptance of the germ theory of disease.*

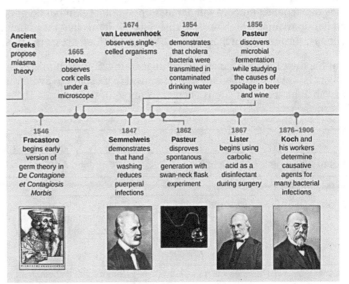

To prevent the spread of human disease, it is necessary to control the growth and abundance of microbes in or on various items frequently used by humans. Inanimate items, such as doorknobs, toys, or towels, which may harbor microbes and aid in disease transmission, are called **fomites**. Two factors heavily influence the level of cleanliness required for a particular fomite and, hence, the protocol chosen to achieve this level. The first factor is the application for which the item will be used. For example, invasive applications that require insertion into the human body require a much higher level of cleanliness than applications that do not. The second factor is the level of resistance to antimicrobial treatment by potential pathogens. For example, foods preserved by canning often become contaminated with the bacterium *Clostridium botulinum*, which produces the neurotoxin that causes botulism. Because *C. botulinum* can produce endospores that can survive harsh conditions, extreme temperatures and pressures must be used to eliminate the endospores. Other organisms may not require such extreme measures and can be controlled by a procedure such as washing clothes in a laundry machine.

Methods of Microbial Control

The most extreme protocols for microbial control aim to achieve **sterilization**: the complete removal or killing of all vegetative cells, endospores, and viruses from the targeted item or environment. Sterilization protocols are generally reserved for laboratory, medical, manufacturing, and food industry settings, where it may be imperative for certain items to be completely free of potentially infectious agents. Sterilization can be accomplished through either physical means, such as exposure to high heat, pressure, or filtration through an appropriate filter, or by chemical means. Chemicals that can be used to achieve sterilization are called sterilants. Sterilants effectively kill all microbes and viruses, and, with appropriate exposure time, can also kill endospores.

For many clinical purposes, **aseptic technique** is necessary to prevent contamination of sterile surfaces. Aseptic technique involves a combination of protocols that collectively maintain sterility, or asepsis, thus preventing contamination of the patient with microbes and infectious agents. Failure to practice aseptic technique during many types of clinical procedures may introduce microbes to the patient's body and put the patient at risk for sepsis, a systemic inflammatory response to an infection that results in high fever, increased heart and respiratory rates, shock, and, possibly, death. Medical procedures that carry risk of contamination must be performed in a sterile field, a designated area that is kept free of all vegetative microbes, endospores, and viruses. Sterile fields are created according to protocols requiring the use of sterilized materials, such as packaging and drapings, and strict procedures for washing and application of sterilants. Other protocols are followed to maintain the sterile field while the medical procedure is being performed.

Sterilization protocols require procedures that are not practical, or necessary, in many settings. Various other methods are used in clinical and nonclinical settings to reduce the microbial load on items. Although the terms for these methods are often used interchangeably, there are important distinctions.

The process of **disinfection** inactivates most microbes on the surface of a fomite by using antimicrobial chemicals or heat. Because some microbes remain, the disinfected item is not considered sterile. Ideally, **disinfectants** should be fast acting, stable, easy to prepare, in-expensive, and easy to use. An example of a natural disinfectant is vinegar; its acidity kills most microbes. Chemical disinfectants, such as chlorine bleach or products containing chlorine, are used to clean nonliving surfaces such as laboratory benches, clinical surfaces, and bathroom sinks. Typical disinfection does not lead to sterilization because endospores tend to survive even when all vegetative cells have been killed.

Unlike disinfectants, **antiseptics** are antimicrobial chemicals safe for use on living skin or tissues. Examples of antiseptics include hydrogen peroxide and isopropyl alcohol. The process of applying an antiseptic is called **antisepsis**. In addition to the characteristics of a good disinfectant, antiseptics must also be selectively effective against microorganisms and able to penetrate tissue deeply without causing tissue damage.

The type of protocol required to achieve the desired level of cleanliness depends on the particular item to be cleaned. For example, those used clinically are categorized as critical, semicritical, and noncritical. Critical items must be sterile because they will be used inside the body, often penetrating sterile tissues or the bloodstream; examples of critical items include surgical instruments, catheters, and intravenous fluids. Gastrointestinal endoscopes and various types of equipment for respiratory therapies are examples of semicritical items; they may contact mucous membranes or nonintact skin but do not penetrate tissues. Semicritical items do not typically need to be sterilized but do require a high level of disinfection. Items that may contact but not penetrate intact skin are noncritical items; examples are bed linens, furniture, crutches, stethoscopes, and blood pressure cuffs. These articles need to be clean but not highly disinfected.

The act of handwashing is an example of **degerming**, in which microbial numbers are significantly reduced by gently scrubbing living tissue, most commonly skin, with a mild chemical (e.g., soap) to avoid the transmission of pathogenic microbes. Wiping the skin with an alcohol swab at an injection site is another example of degerming. These degerming methods remove most (but not all) microbes from the skin's surface.

Common Protocols for Control of Microbial Growth			
Protocol	Definition	Common Application	Common Agents
For Use on Fomites			
Disinfection	Reduces or destroys microbial load of an inanimate item through application of heat or antimicrobial chemicals	Cleaning surfaces like laboratory benches, clinical surfaces, and bathrooms	Chlorine bleach, phenols (e.g., Lysol), glutaraldehyde
Sanitization	Reduces microbial load of an inanimate item to safe public health levels through application of heat or antimicrobial chemicals	Commercial dishwashing of eating utensils, cleaning public restrooms	Detergents containing phosphates (e.g., Finish), industrial-strength cleaners containing quaternary ammonium compounds
Sterilization	Completely eliminates all vegetative cells, endospores, and viruses from an inanimate item	Preparation of surgical equipment and of needles used for injection	Pressurized steam (autoclave), chemicals, radiation
For Use on Living Tissue			
Antisepsis	Reduces microbial load on skin or tissue through application of an antimicrobial chemical	Cleaning skin broken due to injury; cleaning skin before surgery	Boric acid, isopropyl alcohol, hydrogen peroxide, iodine (betadine)
Degerming	Reduces microbial load on skin or tissue through gentle to firm scrubbing and the use of mild chemicals	Handwashing	Soap, alcohol swab

The term **sanitization** refers to the cleansing of fomites to remove enough microbes to achieve levels deemed safe for public health. For example, commercial dishwashers used in the food service industry typically use very hot water and air for washing and drying; the high temperatures kill most microbes, sanitizing the dishes. Surfaces in hospital rooms are commonly sanitized using a chemical disinfectant to prevent disease transmission between patients.

Control of Specific Organisms

Physical and chemical methods of microbial control that kill the targeted microorganism are identified by the suffix -*cide* (or -*cidal*). The prefix indicates the type of microbe or infectious agent killed by the treatment method: **bactericides** kill bacteria, **viricides** kill or inactivate viruses, and **fungicides** kill fungi. Other methods do not kill organisms but, instead, stop their growth, making their population static; such methods are identified by the suffix -*stat* (or -*static*). For example, **bacteriostatic** treatments inhibit the growth of bacteria, whereas **fungistatic** treatments inhibit the growth of fungi. Factors that determine whether a particular treatment is -*cidal* or -*static* include the types of microorganisms targeted, the concentration of the chemical used, and the nature of the treatment applied.

Although -*static* treatments do not actually kill infectious agents, they are often less toxic to humans and other animals, and may also better preserve the integrity of the item treated. Such treatments are typically sufficient to keep the microbial population of an item in check. The reduced toxicity of some of these -*static* chemicals also allows them to be impregnated safely into plastics to prevent the growth of microbes on these surfaces. Such plastics are used in products such as toys for children and cutting boards for food preparation. When used to treat an infection, -*static* treatments are typically sufficient in an otherwise healthy individual, preventing the pathogen from multiplying, thus allowing the individual's immune system to clear the infection.

Conditions that Affect Microbial Control

Several factors contribute to the effectiveness of a disinfecting agent or microbial control protocol. First, the length of time of exposure is important. Longer exposure times kill more microbes. Because microbial death of a population exposed to a specific protocol is logarithmic, it takes longer to kill a high-population load than a low-population load exposed to the same protocol. A shorter treatment time is needed when starting with a smaller number of organisms. Effectiveness also depends on the susceptibility of the agent to that disinfecting agent or protocol. The concentration of disinfecting agent or intensity of exposure is also important. For example, higher temperatures and higher concentrations of disinfectants kill microbes more quickly and effectively. Conditions that limit contact between the agent and the targeted cells cells—for example, the presence of bodily fluids, tissue, organic debris (e.g., mud or feces), or biofilms on surfaces—increase the cleaning time or intensity of the microbial control protocol required to reach the desired level of cleanliness. All these factors must be considered when choosing the appropriate protocol to control microbial growth in a given situation.

Laboratory Biological Safety Levels

For researchers or laboratory personnel working with pathogens, the risks associated with specific pathogens determine the levels of cleanliness and control required. The Centers for Disease Control and Prevention (CDC) and the National Institutes of Health (NIH) have established four classification levels, called "biological safety levels" (BSLs). Various organizations around the world, including the World Health Organization (WHO) and the European Union (EU), use a similar classification scheme. According to the CDC, the BSL is determined by the agent's infectivity, ease of transmission, and potential disease severity, as well as the type of work being done with the agent.

Each BSL requires a different level of biocontainment to prevent contamination and spread of infectious agents to laboratory personnel and, ultimately, the community. For example, the lowest BSL, BSL-1, requires the fewest precautions because it applies to situations with the lowest risk for microbial infection.

BSL-1 agents are those that generally do not cause infection in healthy human adults. These include noninfectious bacteria, such as nonpathogenic strains of *Escherichia coli* and *Bacillus subtilis*, and viruses known to infect animals other than humans, such as baculoviruses (insect viruses). Because working with BSL-1 agents poses very little risk, few precautions are necessary. Laboratory workers use standard aseptic technique and may work with these agents at an open laboratory bench or table, wearing personal protective equipment (PPE) such as a laboratory coat, goggles, and gloves, as needed. Other than a sink for handwashing and doors to separate the laboratory from the rest of the building, no additional modifications are needed.

Agents classified as BSL-2 include those that pose moderate risk to laboratory workers and the community, and are typically "indigenous," meaning that they are commonly found in that geographical area. These include bacteria such as *Staphylococcus aureus* and *Salmonella* spp., and viruses like hepatitis, mumps, and measles viruses. BSL-2 laboratories require additional precautions beyond those of BSL-1, including restricted access; required PPE, including a face shield in some circumstances; and the use of biological safety cabinets for procedures that may disperse agents through the air (called "aerosolization"). BSL-2 laboratories are equipped with self-closing doors, an eyewash station, and an **autoclave**, which is a specialized device for sterilizing materials with pressurized steam before use or disposal. BSL-1 laboratories may also have an autoclave.

BSL-3 agents have the potential to cause lethal infections by inhalation. These may be either indigenous or "exotic," meaning that they are derived from a foreign location, and include pathogens such as *Mycobacterium tuberculosis*, *Bacillus anthracis*, West Nile virus, and human immunodeficiency virus (HIV). Because of the serious nature of the infections caused by BSL-3 agents, laboratories working with them require restricted access. Laboratory workers are under medical surveillance, possibly receiving vaccinations for the microbes with which they work. In addition to the standard PPE already mentioned, laboratory personnel in BSL-3 laboratories must also wear a respirator and work with microbes and infectious agents in a biological safety cabinet at all times. BSL-3 laboratories require a hands-free sink, an eyewash station near the exit, and two sets of self-closing and locking doors at the entrance. These laboratories are equipped with directional airflow, meaning that clean air is pulled through the laboratory from clean areas to potentially contaminated areas. This air cannot be recirculated, so a constant supply of clean air is required.

BSL-4 agents are the most dangerous and often fatal. These microbes are typically exotic, are easily transmitted by inhalation, and cause infections for which there are no treatments or vaccinations. Examples include Ebola virus and Marburg virus, both of which cause hemorrhagic fevers, and smallpox virus. There are only a small number of laboratories in the United States and around the world appropriately equipped to work with these agents. In addition to BSL-3 precautions, laboratory workers in BSL-4 facilities must also change their clothing on entering the laboratory, shower on exiting, and decontaminate all material on exiting. While working in the laboratory, they must either wear a full-body protective suit with a designated air supply or conduct all work within a biological safety cabinet with a high-efficiency particulate air (HEPA)-filtered air supply and a doubly HEPA-filtered exhaust. If wearing a suit, the air pressure within the suit must be higher than that outside the suit, so that if a leak in the suit occurs, laboratory air that may be contaminated cannot be drawn into the suit. The laboratory itself must be located either in a separate building or in an isolated portion of a building and have its own air supply and exhaust system, as well as its own decontamination system.

Figure 3 A protective suit like this one is an additional precaution for those who work in BSL-4 laboratories. This suit has its own air supply and maintains a positive pressure relative to the outside, so that if a leak occurs, air will flow out of the suit, not into it from the laboratory. (credit: modification of work by Centers for Disease Control and Prevention)

Biosafety Levels			
Biological Safety Levels	**Description**	**Examples**	**CDC Classification**
BSL-4	Microbes are dangerous and exotic, posing a high risk of aerosol-transmitted infections, which are frequently fatal without treatment or vaccines. Few labs are at this level.	Ebola and Marburg viruses	
BSL-3	Microbes are indigenous or exotic and cause serious or potentially lethal diseases through respiratory transmission.	*Mycobacterium tuberculosis*	
BSL-2	Microbes are typically indigenous and are associated with diseases of varying severity. They pose moderate risk to workers and the environment.	*Staphylococcus aureus*	
BSL-1	Microbes are not known to cause disease in healthy hosts and pose minimal risk to workers and the environment.	Nonpathogenic strains of *Escherichia coli*	

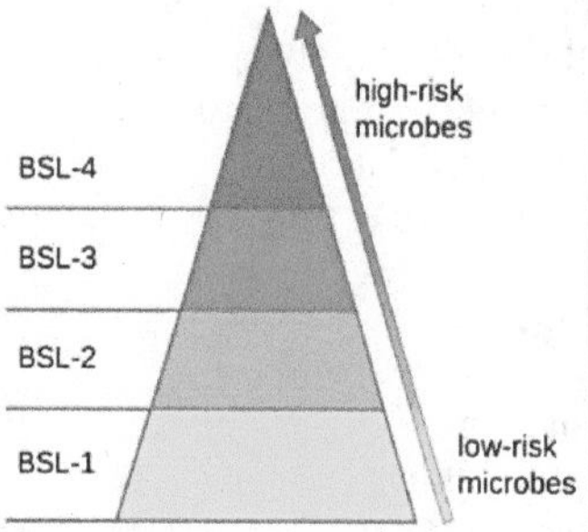

Figure 4 The CDC classifies infectious agents into four biosafety levels based on potential risk to laboratory personnel and the community. Each level requires a progressively greater level of precaution. (credit "pyramid": modification of work by Centers for Disease Control and Prevention)

Using Physical Methods to Control Microorganisms

For thousands of years, humans have used various physical methods of microbial control for food preservation. Common control methods include the application of high temperatures, radiation, filtration, and desiccation (drying), among others. Many of these methods nonspecifically kill cells by disrupting membranes, changing membrane permeability, or damaging proteins and nucleic acids by denaturation, degradation, or chemical modification. Various physical methods used for microbial control are described in this section.

Heat

Heating is one of the most common—and oldest—forms of microbial control. It is used in simple techniques like cooking and canning. Heat can kill microbes by altering their membranes and **denaturing proteins**. Different microorganisms will respond differently to high temperatures, with some (e.g., endospore-formers such as *C. botulinum*) being more heat tolerant. Boiling is one of the oldest methods of moist-heat control of microbes, and it is typically quite effective at killing vegetative cells and some viruses. However, boiling is less effective at killing endospores; some endospores are able to survive up to 20 hours of boiling. Additionally, boiling may be less effective at higher altitudes, where the boiling point of water is lower and the boiling time needed to kill microbes is therefore longer. For these reasons, boiling is not considered a useful sterilization technique in the laboratory or clinical setting.

Many different heating protocols can be used for sterilization in the laboratory or clinic, and these protocols can be broken down into two main categories: **dry-heat sterilization** and **moist-heat sterilization**. Aseptic technique in the laboratory typically involves some dry-heat sterilization protocols using direct application of high heat, such as sterilizing inoculating loops. Incineration at very high temperatures destroys all microorganisms. Dry heat can also be applied for relatively long periods of time (at least 2 hours) at temperatures up to 170 °C by using a dry-heat sterilizer, such as an oven. However, moist-heat sterilization is typically the more effective protocol because it penetrates cells better than dry heat does.

Autoclaves rely on moist-heat sterilization. They are used to raise temperatures above the boiling point of water to sterilize items such as surgical equipment from vegetative cells, viruses, and especially endospores, which are known to survive boiling temperatures, without damaging the items. Charles Chamberland (1851–1908) designed the modern autoclave in 1879 while working in the laboratory of Louis Pasteur. The autoclave is still considered the most effective method of sterilization.

In general, the air in the chamber of an autoclave is removed and replaced with increasing amounts of steam trapped within the enclosed chamber, resulting in increased interior pressure and temperatures above the boiling point of water.

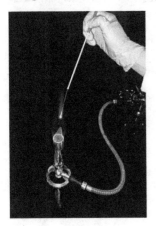 

Figure 5 *(a) Sterilizing a loop, often referred to as "flaming a loop," is a common component of aseptic technique in the microbiology laboratory and is used to incinerate any microorganisms on the loop. (b) Alternatively, a bactericinerator may be used to reduce aerosolization of microbes and remove the presence of an open flame in the laboratory. These are examples of dry-heat sterilization by the direct application of high heat capable of incineration. (credit a: modification of work by Anh-Hue Tu; credit b: modification of work by Brian Forster)*

Standard operating temperatures for autoclaves are 121 °C or, in some cases, 132 °C, typically at a pressure of 15 to 20 pounds per square inch (psi). The length of exposure depends on the volume and nature of material being sterilized, but it is typically 20 minutes or more, with larger volumes requiring longer exposure times to ensure sufficient heat transfer to the materials being sterilized. The steam must directly contact the liquids or dry materials being sterilized, so containers are left loosely closed and instruments are loosely wrapped in paper or foil. The key to autoclaving is that the temperature must be high enough to kill endospores to achieve complete sterilization.

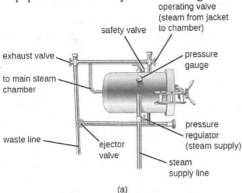 

Figure 6 *(a) An autoclave is commonly used for sterilization in the laboratory and in clinical settings. By displacing the air in the chamber with increasing amounts of steam, pressure increases, and temperatures exceeding 100 °C can be achieved, allowing for complete sterilization. (b) A researcher programs an autoclave to sterilize a sample. (credit a: modification of work by Courtney Harrington; credit b: modification of work by Lackemeyer MG, Kok-Mercado Fd, Wada J, Bollinger L, Kindrachuk J, Wahl-Jensen V, Kuhn JH, Jahrling PB)*

Because sterilization is so important to safe medical and laboratory protocols, quality control is essential. Autoclaves may be equipped with recorders to document the pressures and temperatures achieved during each run. Additionally, internal indicators of various types should be autoclaved along with the materials to be sterilized to ensure that the proper sterilization temperature has been reached.

Although complete sterilization is ideal for many medical applications, it is not always practical for other applications and may also alter the quality of the product. Boiling and autoclaving are not ideal ways to control microbial growth in many foods because these methods may ruin the consistency and other organoleptic (sensory) qualities of the food. **Pasteurization** is a form of microbial control for food that uses

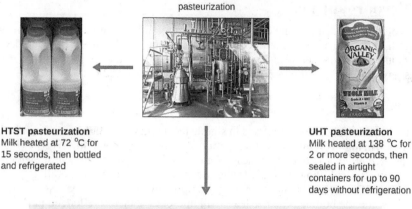

pasteurization

HTST pasteurization
Milk heated at 72 °C for
15 seconds, then bottled
and refrigerated

UHT pasteurization
Milk heated at 138 °C for
2 or more seconds, then
sealed in airtight
containers for up to 90
days without refrigeration

Milkborne organisms killed by pasteurization: *Campylobacter jejuni*, *Coxiella Burnetii*, *Listeria monocytogenes*, *Escherichia coli* O157:H7, *Mycobacterium tuberculosis*, *M. paratuberculosis*, *Salmonella* spp., *Yersinia enterocolitica*

Figure 7 *Two different methods of pasteurization, HTST and UHT, are commonly used to kill pathogens associated with milk spoilage. (credit left: modification of work by Mark Hillary; credit right: modification of work by Kerry Ceszyk)*

heat but does not render the food sterile. Traditional pasteurization kills pathogens and reduces the number of spoilage-causing microbes while maintaining food quality. The process of pasteurization was first developed by Louis Pasteur in the 1860s as a method for preventing the spoilage of beer and wine. Today, pasteurization is most commonly used to kill heat-sensitive pathogens in milk and other food products (e.g., apple juice and honey). However, because pasteurized food products are not sterile, they will eventually spoil. The methods used for milk pasteurization balance the temperature and the length of time of treatment. One method, **high-temperature short-time (HTST) pasteurization**, exposes milk to a temperature of 72 °C for 15 seconds, which lowers bacterial numbers while preserving the quality of the milk. An alternative is ultra-high-temperature (UHT) pasteurization, in which the milk is exposed to a temperature of 138 °C for 2 or more seconds. UHT pasteurized milk can be stored for a long time in sealed containers without being refrigerated; however, the very high temperatures alter the proteins in the milk, causing slight changes in the taste and smell. Still, this method of pasteurization is advantageous in regions where access to refrigeration is limited.

Refrigeration and Freezing

Just as high temperatures are effective for controlling microbial growth, exposing microbes to low temperatures can also be an easy and effective method of microbial control, with the exception of psychrophiles, which prefer cold temperatures. Refrigerators used in home kitchens or in the laboratory maintain temperatures between 0 °C and 7 °C. This temperature range inhibits microbial metabolism, slowing the growth of microorganisms significantly and helping preserve refrigerated products such as foods or medical supplies. Certain types of laboratory cultures can be preserved by refrigeration for later use.

Freezing below −2 °C may stop microbial growth and even kill susceptible organisms. According to the US Department of Agriculture (USDA), the only safe ways that frozen foods can be thawed are in the refrigerator, immersed in cold water changed every 30 minutes, or in the microwave, keeping the food at temperatures not conducive for bacterial growth.[3] In addition, halted bacterial growth can restart in thawed foods, so thawed foods should be treated like fresh perishables.

Bacterial cultures and medical specimens requiring long-term storage or transport are often frozen at ultra-low temperatures of −70 °C or lower. These ultra-low temperatures can be achieved by storing specimens on dry ice in an ultra-low freezer or in special liquid nitrogen tanks, which maintain temperatures lower than −196 °C.

(a)

(b)

Figure 8 *Cultures and other medical specimens can be stored for long periods at ultra-low temperatures. (a) An ultra-low freezer maintains temperatures at or below −70 °C. (b) Even lower temperatures can be achieved through freezing and storage in liquid nitrogen. (credit a: modification of work by "Expert Infantry"/Flickr; credit b: modification of work by USDA)*

Pressure

Exposure to **high pressure** kills many microbes. In the food industry, high-pressure processing (also called pascalization) is used to kill bacteria, yeast, molds, parasites, and viruses in foods while maintaining food quality and extending shelf life. The application of high pressure between 100 and 800 MPa (sea level atmospheric pressure is about 0.1 MPa) is sufficient to kill vegetative cells by protein denaturation, but endospores may survive these pressures.[45]

In clinical settings, hyperbaric oxygen therapy is sometimes used to treat infections. In this form of therapy, a patient breathes pure oxygen at a pressure higher than normal atmospheric pressure, typically between 1 and 3 atmospheres (atm). This is achieved by placing the patient in a hyperbaric chamber or by supplying the pressurized oxygen through a breathing tube. Hyperbaric oxygen therapy helps increase oxygen saturation in tissues that become hypoxic due to infection and inflammation. This increased oxygen concentration enhances the body's immune response by increasing the activities of neutrophils and macrophages, white blood cells that fight infections. Increased oxygen levels also contribute to the formation of toxic free radicals that inhibit the growth of oxygen-sensitive or anaerobic bacteria like as *Clostridium perfringens*, a common cause of gas gangrene. In *C. perfringens* infections, hyperbaric oxygen therapy can also reduce secretion of a bacterial toxin that causes tissue destruction. Hyperbaric oxygen therapy also seems to enhance the effectiveness of antibiotic treatments. Unfortunately, some rare risks include oxygen toxicity and effects on delicate tissues, such as the eyes, middle ear, and lungs, which may be damaged by the increased air pressure.

High pressure processing is not commonly used for disinfection or sterilization of fomites. Although the application of pressure and steam in an autoclave is effective for killing endospores, it is the high temperature achieved, and not the pressure directly, that results in endospore death.

Desiccation

Drying, also known as **desiccation** or dehydration, is a method that has been used for millennia to preserve foods such as raisins, prunes, and jerky. It works because all cells, including microbes, require water for their metabolism and survival. Although drying controls microbial growth, it might not kill all microbes or their endospores, which may start to regrow when conditions are more favorable and water content is restored.

In some cases, foods are dried in the sun, relying on evaporation to achieve desiccation. **Freeze-drying**, or **lyophilization**, is another method of dessication in which an item is rapidly frozen ("snap-frozen") and placed under vacuum so that water is lost by sublimation. Lyophilization combines both exposure to cold temperatures and desiccation, making it quite effective for controlling microbial growth. In addition, lyophilization causes less damage to an item than conventional desiccation and better preserves the item's original qualities. Lyophilized items may be stored at room temperature if packaged appropriately to prevent moisture acquisition. Lyophilization is used for preservation in the food industry and is also used in the laboratory for the long-term storage and transportation of microbial cultures.

The water content of foods and materials, called the water activity, can be lowered without physical drying by the addition of solutes such as salts or sugars. At very high concentrations of salts or sugars, the amount of available water in microbial cells is reduced dramatically because water will be drawn from an area of low solute concentration (inside the cell) to an area of high solute concentration (outside the cell) . Many microorganisms do not survive these conditions of high osmotic pressure. Honey, for example, is 80% sucrose, an environment in which very few microorganisms are capable of growing, thereby eliminating the need for refrigeration. Salted meats and fish, like ham and cod, respectively, were critically important foods before the age of refrigeration. Fruits were preserved by adding sugar, making jams and jellies. However, certain microbes, such as molds and yeasts, tend to be more tolerant of desiccation and high osmotic pressures, and, thus, may still contaminate these types of foods.

(a)   (b)

Figure 9 (a) The addition of a solute creates a hypertonic environment, drawing water out of cells. (b) Some foods can be dried directly, like raisins and jerky. Other foods are dried with the addition of salt, as in the case of salted fish, or sugar, as in the case of jam. (credit a: modification of work by "Bruce Blaus"/Wikimedia Commons; credit raisins: modification of work by Christian Schnettelker; credit jerky: modification of work by Larry Jacobsen; credit salted fish: modification of work by "The Photographer"/Wikimedia Commons; credit jam: modification of work by Kim Becker)

Radiation

Radiation in various forms, from high-energy radiation to sunlight, can be used to kill microbes or inhibit their growth. Ionizing and nonionizing radiation can both be used for microbial control. **Ionizing radiation** includes **X-rays** and **gamma rays**. Ionizing radiation is strong enough to pass into the cell, where it alters molecular structures and damages cell components. For example, ionizing radiation introduces double-strand breaks in DNA molecules. This may directly cause DNA mutations to occur, or mutations may be introduced when the cell attempts to repair the DNA damage. As these mutations accumulate, they eventually lead to cell death.

Both X-rays and gamma rays easily penetrate paper and plastic and can therefore be used to sterilize many packaged materials. In the laboratory, ionizing radiation is commonly used to sterilize materials that cannot be autoclaved, such as plastic Petri dishes and disposable plastic inoculating loops. For clinical use, ionizing radiation is used to sterilize gloves, intravenous tubing, and other latex and plastic items used for patient care. Ionizing radiation is also used for the sterilization of other types of delicate, heat-sensitive materials used clinically, including tissues for transplantation, pharmaceutical drugs, and medical equipment.

In Europe, gamma irradiation for food preservation is widely used, although it has been slow to catch on in the United States. Packaged dried spices are also often gamma-irradiated. Because of their ability to penetrate paper, plastic, thin sheets of wood and metal, and tissue, great care must be taken when using X-rays and gamma irradiation. These types of ionizing irradiation cannot penetrate thick layers of iron or lead, so these metals are commonly used to protect humans who may be potentially exposed.

Another type of radiation, **nonionizing radiation**, is commonly used for disinfection and uses less energy than ionizing radiation. It does not penetrate cells or packaging. **Ultraviolet (UV) light** is one example that leads to formation of mutations that can ultimately kill microorganisms.

UV light can be used effectively by both consumers and laboratory personnel to control microbial growth. UV lamps are now commonly incorporated into water purification systems for use in homes. In addition, small portable UV lights are commonly used by campers to purify water from natural environments before drinking. Germicidal lamps are also used in surgical suites, biological safety cabinets, and transfer hoods, typically emitting UV light at a wavelength of 260 nm. Because UV light does not penetrate surfaces and will not pass through plastics or glass, cells must be exposed directly to the light source.

Filtration

Filtration is a method of physically separating microbes from samples. Air is commonly filtered **through high-efficiency particulate air (HEPA)** filters. HEPA filters have effective pore sizes of 0.3 μm, small enough to capture bacterial cells, endospores, and many viruses, as air passes through these filters, nearly sterilizing the air on the other side of the filter. HEPA filters have a variety of applications and are used widely in clinical settings, in cars and airplanes, and even in the home. For example, they may be found in vacuum cleaners, heating and air-conditioning systems, and air purifiers.

(a)

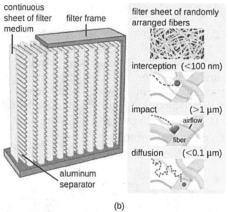

(b)

Biological safety cabinets are a good example of the use of HEPA filters. HEPA filters in biological safety cabinets (BSCs) are used to remove particulates in the air either entering the cabinet (air intake), leaving the cabinet (air exhaust), or treating both the intake and exhaust. Use of an air-intake HEPA filter prevents environmental contaminants from entering the BSC, creating a clean area for handling biological materials. Use of an air-exhaust HEPA filter prevents laboratory pathogens from contaminating the laboratory, thus maintaining a safe work area for laboratory personnel.

Figure 10 *(a) HEPA filters like this one remove microbes, endospores, and viruses as air flows through them. (b) A schematic of a HEPA filter. (credit a: modification of work by CSIRO; credit b: modification of work by "LadyofHats"/Mariana Ruiz Villareal)*

HEPA filters are also commonly used in hospitals and surgical suites to prevent contamination and the spread of airborne microbes through ventilation systems. HEPA filtration systems may be designed for entire buildings or for individual rooms. For example, burn units, operating rooms, or isolation units may require special HEPA-filtration systems to remove opportunistic pathogens from the environment because patients in these rooms are particularly vulnerable to infection.

Filtration can also be used to remove microbes from liquid samples using **membrane filtration**. Membrane filters for liquids function similarly to HEPA filters for air. Typically, membrane filters that are used to remove bacteria have an effective pore size of 0.2 μm, smaller than the average size of a bacterium (1 μm), but filters with smaller pore sizes are available for more specific needs. Membrane filtration is useful for removing bacteria from various types of heat-sensitive solutions used in the laboratory, such as antibiotic solutions and vitamin solutions. Large volumes of culture media may also be filter sterilized rather than autoclaved to protect heat-sensitive components. Often when filtering small volumes, syringe filters are used, but vacuum filters are typically used for filtering larger volumes.

(a)

(b)

Figure 11 *Membrane filters come in a variety of sizes, depending on the volume of solution being filtered. (a) Larger volumes are filtered in units like these. The solution is drawn through the filter by connecting the unit to a vacuum. (b) Smaller volumes are often filtered using syringe filters, which are units that fit on the end of a syringe. In this case, the solution is pushed through by depressing the syringe's plunger. (credit a, b: modification of work by Brian Forster)*

Physical Methods of Control			
Method	Conditions	Mode of Action	Example Uses
Heat			
Boiling	100 °C at sea level	Denatures proteins and alters membranes	Cooking, personal use, preparing certain laboratory media
Dry-heat oven	170 °C for 2 hours	Denatures proteins and alters membranes, dehydration, desiccation	Sterilization of heat-stable medical and laboratory equipment and glassware
Incineration	Exposure to flame	Destroy by burning	Flaming loop, microincinerator
Autoclave	Typical settings: 121 °C for 15 minutes at 15 pounds per square inch (psi)	Denatures proteins and alters membranes	Sterilization of microbiological media, heat-stable medical and laboratory equipment, and other heat-stable items
Pasteurization	Can vary. One type is 72 °C for 15 seconds (HTST)	Denatures proteins and alters membranes	Prevents spoilage of milk, apple juice, honey, and other ingestible liquids
Cold			
Refrigeration	0 °C to 7 °C	Inhibits metabolism (slows or arrests cell division)	Preservation of food or laboratory materials (solutions, cultures)
Freezing	Below −2 °C	Stops metabolism, may kill microbes	Long-term storage of food, laboratory cultures, or medical specimens
Pressure			
High-pressure processing	100–800 MPa	Denatures proteins and can cause cell lysis	Preservation of food
Hyberbaric oxygen therapy	Air pressure three times higher than normal	Inhibits metabolism and growth of anaerobic microbes	Treatment of certain infections (e.g., gas gangrene)
Desiccation			
Simple desiccation	Drying	Inhibits metabolism	Dried fruits, jerky
Reduce water activity	Addition of salt or water	Inhibits metabolism and can cause lysis	Salted meats and fish, honey, jams and jellies
Lyophilization	Rapid freezing under vacuum	Inhibits metabolism	Preservation of food, laboratory cultures, or reagents
Radiation			
Ionizing radiation	Exposure to X-rays or gamma rays	Alters molecular structures, introduces double-strand breaks into DNA	Sterilization of spices and heat-sensitive laboratory and medical items; used for food sterilization in Europe but not widely accepted in US
Nonionizing radiation	Exposure to ultraviolet light	Introduces thymine dimers, leading to mutations	Disinfection of surfaces in laboratories and rooms in health-care environment, and disinfection of water and air

Physical Methods of Control (continued)			
Method	Conditions	Mode of Action	Example Uses
Sonication			
Sonication	Exposure to ultrasonic waves	Cavitation (formation of empty space) disrupts cells, lysing them	Laboratory research to lyse cells; cleaning jewelry, lenses, and equipment
Filtration			
HEPA filtration	Use of high-efficiency particulate air (HEPA) filter with 0.3 μm pore size	Physically removes microbes from air	Laboratory biological safety cabinets, operating rooms, isolation units, heating and air conditioning systems, vacuum cleaners
Membrane filtration	Use of membrane filter with 0.2-μm or smaller pore size	Physically removes microbes from liquid solutions	Removal of bacteria from heat-sensitive solutions like vitamins, antibiotics, and media with heat-sensitive components

Using Chemicals to Control Microorganisms

In addition to physical methods of microbial control, chemicals are also used to control microbial growth. A wide variety of chemicals can be used as disinfectants or antiseptics. When choosing which to use, it is important to consider the type of microbe targeted; how clean the item needs to be; the disinfectant's effect on the item's integrity; its safety to animals, humans, and the environment; its expense; and its ease of use. This section describes the variety of chemicals used as disinfectants and antiseptics, including their mechanisms of action and common uses.

Phenolics

In the 1800s, scientists began experimenting with a variety of chemicals for disinfection. In the 1860s, British surgeon **Joseph** Lister (1827–1912) began using carbolic acid, known as phenol, as a disinfectant for the treatment of surgical wounds. In 1879, Lister's work inspired the American chemist Joseph Lawrence (1836–1909) to develop Listerine, an alcohol-based mixture of several related compounds that is still used today as an oral antiseptic. Today, carbolic acid is no longer used as a surgical disinfectant because it is a skin irritant, but the chemical compounds found in antiseptic mouthwashes and throat lozenges are called phenolics.

Chemically, phenol consists of a benzene ring with an –OH group, and **phenolics** are compounds that have this group as part of their chemical structure. Phenolics such as thymol and eucalyptol occur naturally in plants. Other phenolics can be derived from creosote, a component of coal tar. Phenolics tend to be stable, persistent on surfaces, and less toxic than phenol. They inhibit microbial growth by denaturing proteins and disrupting membranes.

Figure 12 *Phenol and phenolic compounds have been used to control microbial growth. (a) Chemical structure of phenol, also known as carbolic acid. (b) o-Phenylphenol, a type of phenolic, has been used as a disinfectant as well as to control bacterial and fungal growth on harvested citrus fruits. (c) Hexachlorophene, another phenol, known as a bisphenol (two rings), is the active ingredient in pHisoHex.*

Since Lister's time, several phenolic compounds have been used to control microbial growth. Phenolics like cresols (methylated phenols) and o-phenylphenol were active ingredients in various formulations of Lysol since its invention in 1889. o-Phenylphenol was also commonly used in agriculture to control bacterial and fungal growth on harvested crops, especially citrus fruits, but its use in the United States is now far more limited. The bisphenol hexachlorophene, a disinfectant, is the active ingredient in pHisoHex, a topical cleansing detergent widely used for handwashing in hospital settings. pHisoHex is particularly effective against gram-positive bacteria, including those causing staphylococcal and streptococcal skin infections. pHisoHex was formerly used for bathing infants, but this practice has been discontinued because it has been shown that exposure to hexachlorophene can lead to neurological problems.

Triclosan is another bisphenol compound that has seen widespread application in antibacterial products over the last several decades. Initially used in toothpastes, triclosan is now commonly used in hand soaps and is frequently impregnated into a wide variety of other products, including cutting boards, knives, shower curtains, clothing, and concrete, to make them antimicrobial. It is particularly effective against gram-positive bacteria on the skin, as well as certain gram-negative bacteria and yeasts.[8]

Heavy Metals

Some of the first chemical disinfectants and antiseptics to be used were heavy metals. Heavy metals kill microbes by binding to proteins, thus inhibiting enzymatic activity. Heavy metals are oligodynamic, meaning that very small concentrations show significant antimicrobial activity. Ions of heavy metals bind to sulfur-containing amino acids strongly and bioaccumulate within cells, allowing these metals to reach high localized concentrations. This causes proteins to denature.

Heavy metals are not selectively toxic to microbial cells. They may bioaccumulate in human or animal cells, as well, and excessive concentrations can have toxic effects on humans. If too much silver accumulates in the body, for example, it can result in a condi-

   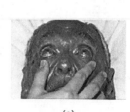

Figure 13 *Heavy metals denature proteins, impairing cell function and, thus, giving them strong antimicrobial properties. (a) Copper in fixtures like this door handle kills microbes that otherwise might accumulate on frequently touched surfaces. (b) Eating utensils contain small amounts of silver to inhibit microbial growth. (c) Copper commonly lines incubators to minimize contamination of cell cultures stored inside. (d) Antiseptic mouthwashes commonly contain zinc chloride. (e) This patient is suffering from argyria, an irreversible condition caused by bioaccumulation of silver in the body. (credit b: modification of work by "Shoshanah"/Flickr; credit e: modification of work by Herbert L. Fred and Hendrik A. van Dijk)*

tion called argyria, in which the skin turns irreversibly blue-gray. One way to reduce the potential toxicity of heavy metals is by carefully controlling the duration of exposure and concentration of the heavy metal.

Silver has long been used as an antiseptic. In ancient times, drinking water was stored in silver jugs. Silvadene cream is commonly used to treat topical wounds and is particularly helpful in preventing infection in burn wounds. Silver nitrate drops were once routinely applied to the eyes of newborns to protect against ophthalmia neonatorum, eye infections that can occur due to exposure to pathogens in the birth canal, but antibiotic creams are more now commonly used. Silver is often combined with antibiotics, making the antibiotics thousands of times more effective.[16] Silver is also commonly incorporated into catheters and bandages, rendering them antimicrobial; however, there is evidence that heavy metals may also enhance selection for antibiotic resistance.[17]

Several other heavy metals also exhibit antimicrobial activity. **Copper sulfate** is a common algicide used to control algal growth in swimming pools and fish tanks. The use of metallic copper to minimize microbial growth is also becoming more widespread. Copper linings in incubators help reduce contamination of cell cultures. The use of copper pots for water storage in underdeveloped countries is being investigated as a way to combat diarrheal diseases. Copper coatings are also becoming popular for frequently handled objects such as doorknobs, cabinet hardware, and other fixtures in health-care facilities in an attempt to reduce the spread of microbes.

Nickel and zinc coatings are now being used in a similar way. Other forms of zinc, including zinc chloride and zinc oxide, are also used commercially. Zinc chloride is quite safe for humans and is commonly found in mouthwashes, substantially increasing their length of effectiveness. Zinc oxide is found in a variety of products, including topical antiseptic creams such as calamine lotion, diaper ointments, baby powder, and dandruff shampoos.

Halogens

Other chemicals commonly used for disinfection are the halogens iodine and chlorine. **Iodine** works by oxidizing cellular components, including sulfur-containing amino acids, nucleotides, and fatty acids, and destabilizing the macromolecules that contain these molecules. It is often used as a topical tincture, but it may cause staining or skin irritation. An **iodophor** is a compound of iodine complexed with an organic molecule, thereby increasing iodine's stability and, in turn, its efficacy. One common iodophor is povidone-iodine, which includes a wetting agent that releases iodine relatively slowly. Betadine is a brand of povidone-iodine commonly used as a hand scrub by medical personnel before surgery and for topical antisepsis of a patient's skin before incision.

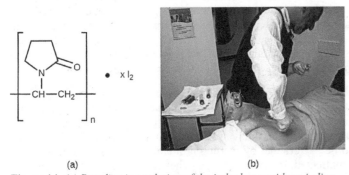

(a)   (b)

Figure 14 *(a) Betadine is a solution of the iodophor povidone-iodine. (b) It is commonly used as a topical antiseptic on a patient's skin before incision during surgery. (credit b: modification of work by Andrew Ratto)*

Chlorine is another halogen commonly used for disinfection. When chlorine gas is mixed with water, it produces a strong oxidant called hypochlorous acid, which is uncharged and enters cells easily. Chlorine gas is commonly used in municipal drinking water and wastewater treatment plants, with the resulting hypochlorous acid producing the actual antimicrobial effect. Those working at water treatment facilities need to take great care to minimize personal exposure to chlorine gas. Sodium hypochlorite is the chemical component of common household bleach, and it is also used for a wide variety of disinfecting purposes. Hypochlorite salts, including sodium and calcium hypochlorites, are used to disinfect swimming pools. Chlorine gas, sodium hypochlorite, and calcium hypochlorite are also commonly used disinfectants in the food processing and restaurant industries to reduce the spread of foodborne diseases. Workers in these industries also need to take care to use these products correctly to ensure their own safety as well as the safety of consumers. A recent joint statement published by the Food and Agriculture Organization (FAO) of the United Nations and WHO indicated that none of the many beneficial uses of chlorine products in food processing to reduce the spread of foodborne illness posed risks to consumers.

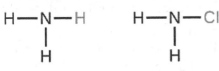

ammonia   chloramine

Figure 15 *Monochloroamine, one of the chloramines, is derived from ammonia by the replacement of one hydrogen atom with a chlorine atom.*

Another class of chlorinated compounds called chloramines are widely used as disinfectants. Chloramines are relatively stable, releasing chlorine over long periods time. Chloramines are derivatives of ammonia by substitution of one, two, or all three hydrogen atoms with chlorine atoms .

Chloramines and other cholorine compounds may be used for disinfection of drinking water, and chloramine tablets are frequently used by the military for this purpose. After a natural disaster or other event that compromises the public water supply, the CDC recommends disinfecting tap water by adding small amounts of regular household bleach.

Although chlorinated compounds are relatively effective disinfectants, they have their disadvantages. Some may irritate the skin, nose, or eyes of some individuals, and they may not completely eliminate certain hardy organisms from contaminated drinking water. The protozoan parasite *Cryptosporidium*, for example, has a protective outer shell that makes it resistant to chlorinated disinfectants. Thus, boiling of drinking water in emergency situations is recommended when possible.

Alcohols

Alcohols make up another group of chemicals commonly used as disinfectants and antiseptics. They work by rapidly denaturing proteins, which inhibits cell metabolism, and by disrupting membranes, which leads to cell lysis. Once denatured, the proteins may potentially refold if enough water is present in the solution. Alcohols are typically used at concentrations of about 70% aqueous solution and, in fact, work better in aqueous solutions than 100% alcohol solutions. This is because alcohols coagulate proteins. In higher alcohol concentrations, rapid coagulation of surface proteins prevents effective penetration of cells. The most commonly used alcohols for disinfection are ethyl alcohol (ethanol) and isopropyl alcohol (isopropanol, rubbing alcohol).

Alcohols tend to be bactericidal and fungicidal, but may also be viricidal for enveloped viruses only. Although alcohols are not sporicidal, they do inhibit the processes of sporulation and germination. Alcohols are volatile and dry quickly, but they may also cause skin irritation because they dehydrate the skin at the site of application. One common clinical use of alcohols is swabbing the skin for degerming before needle injection. Alcohols also are the active ingredients in instant hand sanitizers, which have gained popularity in recent years. The alcohol in these hand sanitizers works both by denaturing proteins and by disrupting the microbial cell membrane, but will not work effectively in the presence of visible dirt.

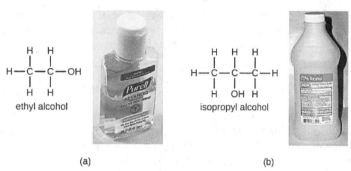

(a)   (b)

Figure 16 *(a) Ethyl alcohol, the intoxicating ingredient found in alcoholic drinks, is also used commonly as a disinfectant. (b) Isopropyl alcohol, also called rubbing alcohol, has a related molecular structure and is another commonly used disinfectant. (credit a photo: modification of work by D Coetzee; credit b photo: modification of work by Craig Spurrier)*

Last, alcohols are used to make tinctures with other antiseptics, such as the iodine tinctures discussed previously in this chapter. All in all, alcohols are inexpensive and quite effective for the disinfection of a broad range of vegetative microbes. However, one disadvantage of alcohols is their high volatility, limiting their effectiveness to immediately after application.

Surfactants

Surface-active agents, or **surfactants**, are a group of chemical compounds that lower the surface tension of water. Surfactants are the major ingredients in soaps and detergents. **Soaps** can interact with oils and grease to create emulsions in water, loosening and lifting away dirt and microbes from surfaces and skin. Soaps do not kill or inhibit microbial growth and so are not considered antiseptics or disinfectants. However, proper use of soaps mechanically carries away microorganisms, effectively degerming a surface. Some soaps contain added bacteriostatic agents such as triclocarban or cloflucarban, compounds structurally related to triclosan that introduce antiseptic or disinfectant properties to the soaps.

Soaps, however, often form films that are difficult to rinse away, especially in hard water, which contains high concentrations of calcium and magnesium mineral salts. **Detergents** contain synthetic surfactant molecules with both polar and nonpolar regions that have strong cleansing activity but are more soluble, even in hard water, and, therefore, leave behind no soapy deposits. An important class of disinfectants and antiseptics called the **quaternary ammonium salts (quats)**. Quats have several useful properties. They are stable, nontoxic, inexpensive, colorless, odorless, and tasteless. They tend to be bactericidal by disrupting membranes. They are also active against fungi, protozoans, and enveloped viruses, but endospores are unaffected. In clinical settings, they may be used as antiseptics or to disinfect surfaces. Mixtures of quats are also commonly found in household cleaners and disinfectants, including many current formulations of Lysol brand products, which contain benzalkonium chlorides as the active ingredients. Benzalkonium chlorides, along with the quat cetylpyridimine chloride, are also found in products such as skin antiseptics, oral rinses, and mouthwashes.

Handwashing the Right Way

Handwashing is critical for public health and should be emphasized in a clinical setting. For the general public, the CDC recommends handwashing before, during, and after food handling; before eating; before and after interacting with someone who is ill; before and after treating a wound; after using the toilet or changing diapers; after coughing, sneezing, or blowing the nose; after handling garbage; and after interacting with an animal, its feed, or its waste.

Handwashing is even more important for health-care workers, who should wash their hands thoroughly between every patient contact, after the removal of gloves, after contact with bodily fluids and potentially infectious fomites, and before and after assisting a surgeon with invasive procedures. Even with the use of proper surgical attire, including gloves, scrubbing for surgery is more involved than routine handwashing. The goal of surgical scrubbing is to reduce the normal microbiota on the skin's surface to prevent the introduction of these microbes into a patient's surgical wounds.

There is no single widely accepted protocol for surgical scrubbing. Protocols for length of time spent scrubbing may depend on the antimicrobial used; health-care workers should always check the manufacturer's recommendations. According to the Association of Surgical Technologists (AST), surgical scrubs may be performed with or without the use of brushes.

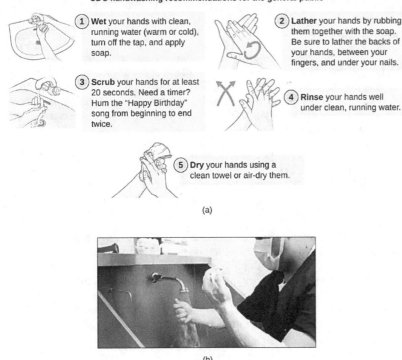

CDC handwashing recommendations for the general public

1. **Wet** your hands with clean, running water (warm or cold), turn off the tap, and apply soap.
2. **Lather** your hands by rubbing them together with the soap. Be sure to lather the backs of your hands, between your fingers, and under your nails.
3. **Scrub** your hands for at least 20 seconds. Need a timer? Hum the "Happy Birthday" song from beginning to end twice.
4. **Rinse** your hands well under clean, running water.
5. **Dry** your hands using a clean towel or air-dry them.

(a)

(b)

Figure 17 *(a) The CDC recommends five steps as part of typical handwashing for the general public. (b) Surgical scrubbing is more extensive, requiring scrubbing starting from the fingertips, extending to the hands and forearms, and then up beyond the elbows, as shown here. (credit a: modification of work by World Health Organization)*

Bisbiguanides

Bisbiguanides were first synthesized in the 20th century and are cationic (positively charged) molecules known for their antiseptic properties . One important bisbiguanide antiseptic is chlorhexidine. It has broad-spectrum activity against yeasts, gram-positive bacteria, and gram-negative bacteria, with the exception of *Pseudomonas aeruginosa*, which may develop resistance on repeated exposure. However, chlorhexidine is poorly effective against *Mycobacterium tuberculosis* and non-enveloped viruses, and it is not sporicidal. Chlorhexidine is typically used in the clinical setting as a surgical scrub and for other handwashing needs for medical personnel, as well as for topical antisepsis for patients before surgery or needle injection. Chlorhexidine solutions may also be used as oral rinses after oral procedures or to treat gingivitis. Another bisbiguanide, alexidine, is gaining popularity as a surgical scrub and an oral rinse because it acts faster than chlorhexidine.

Alkylating Agents – Formaldehyde, glutaraldehyde and ethylene oxide

The alkylating agents are a group of strong disinfecting chemicals that act by replacing a hydrogen atom within a molecule with an alkyl group (C_nH_{2n+1}), thereby inactivating enzymes and nucleic acids . The alkylating agent **formaldehyde** (CH_2OH) is commonly used in solution at a concentration of 37% (known as formalin) or as a gaseous disinfectant and biocide. It is a strong, broad-spectrum disinfectant and biocide that has the ability to kill bacteria, viruses, fungi, and endospores, leading to sterilization at low temperatures, which is sometimes a convenient alternative to the more labor-intensive heat sterilization methods. It also cross-links proteins and has been widely used as a chemical fixative. Because of this, it is used for the storage of tissue specimens and as an embalming fluid. It also has been used to inactivate infectious agents in vaccine preparation. Formaldehyde is very irritating to living tissues and is also carcinogenic; therefore, it is not used as an antiseptic.

Glutaraldehyde is structurally similar to formaldehyde but has two reactive aldehyde groups, allowing it to act more quickly than formaldehyde. It is commonly used as a 2% solution for sterilization and is marketed under the brand name Cidex. It is used to disinfect a variety of surfaces and surgical and medical equipment. However, similar to formaldehyde, glutaraldehyde irritates the skin and is not used as an antiseptic.

A new type of disinfectant gaining popularity for the disinfection of medical equipment is o-phthalaldehyde (OPA), which is found in some newer formulations of Cidex and similar products, replacing glutaraldehyde. o-Phthalaldehyde is thought to work similarly to glutaraldehyde and formaldehyde, but is much less irritating to skin and nasal passages, produces a minimal odor, does not require processing before use, and is more effective against mycobacteria.

Ethylene oxide is a type of alkylating agent that is used for gaseous sterilization. It is highly penetrating and can sterilize items within plastic bags such as catheters, disposable items in laboratories and clinical settings (like packaged Petri dishes), and other pieces of equipment. Ethylene oxide exposure is a form of cold sterilization, making it useful for the sterilization of heat-sensitive items. Great care needs to be taken with the use of ethylene oxide, however; it is carcinogenic, like the other alkylating agents, and is also highly explosive. With careful use and proper aeration of the products after treatment, ethylene oxide is highly effective, and ethylene oxide sterilizers are commonly found in medical settings for sterilizing packaged materials.

Hydrogen peroxide

Hydrogen peroxide is a strong oxidizing agent that can be used as disinfectants or antiseptics. It is often used in solution to disinfect surfaces and may also be used as a gaseous agent. Hydrogen peroxide solutions are inexpensive skin antiseptics that break down into water and oxygen gas, both of which are environmentally safe. This decomposition is accelerated in the presence of light, so hydrogen peroxide solutions typically are sold in brown or opaque bottles. One disadvantage of using hydrogen peroxide as an antiseptic is that it also causes damage to skin that may delay healing or lead to scarring. Contact lens cleaners often include hydrogen peroxide as a disinfectant.

Hydrogen peroxide works by producing free radicals that damage cellular macromolecules. Hydrogen peroxide has broad-spectrum activity, working against gram-positive and gram-negative bacteria (with slightly greater efficacy against gram-positive bacteria), fungi, viruses, and endospores. However, bacteria that produce the oxygen-detoxifying enzymes catalase or peroxidase may have inherent tolerance to low hydrogen peroxide concentrations. To kill endospores, the length of exposure or concentration of solutions of hydrogen peroxide must be increased. Gaseous hydrogen peroxide has greater efficacy and can be used as a sterilant for rooms or equipment.

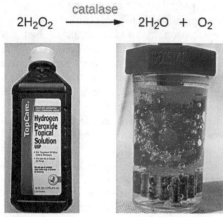

$$2H_2O_2 \xrightarrow{\text{catalase}} 2H_2O + O_2$$

Figure 18 *Catalase enzymatically converts highly reactive hydrogen peroxide (H_2O_2) into water and oxygen. Hydrogen peroxide can be used to clean wounds. Hydrogen peroxide is used to sterilize items such as contact lenses. (credit photos: modification of work by Kerry Ceszyk)*

Supercritical Fluids

Within the last 15 years, the use of **supercritical fluids,** especially supercritical carbon dioxide (scCO_2), has gained popularity for certain sterilizing applications. When carbon dioxide is brought to approximately 10 times atmospheric pressure, it reaches a supercritical state that has physical properties between those of liquids and gases. Materials put into a chamber in which carbon dioxide is pressurized in this way can be sterilized because of the ability of scCO_2 to penetrate surfaces.

Supercritical carbon dioxide works by penetrating cells and forming carbonic acid, thereby lowering the cell pH considerably. This technique is effective against vegetative cells and is also used in combination with peracetic acid to kill endospores. Its efficacy can also be augmented with increased temperature or by rapid cycles of pressurization and depressurization, which more likely produce cell lysis.

Benefits of scCO_2 include the nonreactive, nontoxic, and nonflammable properties of carbon dioxide, and this protocol is effective at low temperatures. Unlike other methods, such as heat and irradiation, that can degrade the object being sterilized, the use of scCO_2 preserves the object's integrity and is commonly used for treating foods (including spices and juices) and medical devices such as endoscopes. It is also gaining popularity for disinfecting tissues such as skin, bones, tendons, and ligaments prior to transplantation. scCO_2 can also be used for pest control because it can kill insect eggs and larvae within products.

Chemical Food Preservatives

Chemical preservatives are used to inhibit microbial growth and minimize spoilage in some foods. Commonly used chemical preservatives include sorbic acid, benzoic acid, and propionic acid, and their more soluble salts potassium sorbate, sodium benzoate, and calcium propionate, all of which are used to control the growth of molds in acidic foods. Each of these preservatives is nontoxic and readily metabolized by humans. They are also flavorless, so they do not compromise the flavor of the foods they preserve.

Sorbic acid is added as a preservative in a wide variety of foods, including dairy, bread, fruit, and vegetable products. Benzoic acid is found naturally in many types of fruits and berries, spices, and fermented products. Foods preserved with benzoic acid or sodium benzoate include fruit juices, jams, ice creams, pastries, soft drinks, chewing gum, and pickles.

Propionic acid is a more effective preservative at a higher pH than either sorbic acid or benzoic acid. Propionic acid is naturally produced by some cheeses during their ripening and is added to other types of cheese and baked goods to prevent mold contamination. It is also added to raw dough to prevent contamination by the bacterium *Bacillus mesentericus*, which causes bread to become ropy.

Other commonly used chemical preservatives include sulfur dioxide and nitrites. Sulfur dioxide prevents browning of foods and is used for the preservation of dried fruits; it has been used in winemaking since ancient times. Sulfur dioxide gas dissolves in water readily, forming sulfites. Although sulfites can be metabolized by the body, some people have sulfite allergies, including asthmatic reactions.

Nitrites are added to processed meats to maintain color and stop the germination of *Clostridium botulinum* endospores. Nitrosamines, however, are carcinogenic and can be produced through exposure of nitrite-preserved meats (e.g., hot dogs, lunch meat, breakfast sausage, bacon, meat in canned soups) to heat during cooking.

Chemical Disinfectants		
Chemical	**Mode of Action**	**Example Uses**
Phenolics		
Cresols o-Phenylphenol Hexachlorophene Triclosan	Denature proteins and disrupt membranes	Disinfectant in Lysol Prevent contamination of crops (citrus) Antibacterial soap pHisoHex for handwashing in hospitals
Metals		
Mercury Silver Copper Nickel Zinc	Bind to proteins and inhibit enzyme activity	Topical antiseptic Treatment of wounds and burns Prevention of eye infections in newborns Antibacterial in catheters and bandages Mouthwash Algicide for pools and fish tanks Containers for water storage
Halogens		
Iodine Chlorine Fluorine	Oxidation and destabilization of cellular macromolecules	Topical antiseptic Hand scrub for medical personnel Water disinfectant Water treatment plants Household bleach Food processing Prevention of dental carries
Alcohols		
Ethanol Isopropanol	Denature proteins and disrupt membranes	Disinfectant Antiseptic
Surfactants		
Quaternary ammonium salts	Lowers surface tension of water to help with washing away of microbes, and disruption of cell membranes	Soaps and detergent Disinfectant Antiseptic Mouthwash
Bisbiguanides		
	Disruption of cell membranes	Oral rinse Hand scrub for medical personnel
Alkylating Agents		
Formaldehyde Glutaraldehyde Ethylene oxide	Inactivation of enzymes and nucleic acid	Disinfectant Tissue specimen storage Embalming Sterilization of medical equipment Vaccine component for sterility
Hydrogen peroxide (and other peroxygens)	Oxidation and destabilization of cellular macromolecules	Antiseptic Disinfectant Acne medication Toothpaste ingredient
Supercritical Gases		
Carbon dioxide	Penetrates cells, forms carbonic acid, lowers intracellular pH	Food preservation Disinfection of medical devices Disinfection of transplant tissues
Chemical Food Preservatives		
Sorbic acid Benzoic acid Propionic acid Potassium sorbate Sodium benzoate Calcium propionate Sulfur dioxide Nitrites	Decrease pH and inhibit enzymatic function	Preservation of food products

Control of Microorganisms in the Body – Antimicrobial Drugs and Vaccines

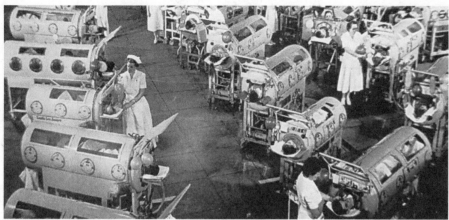

Figure 1 Polio was once a common disease with potentially serious consequences, including paralysis. Vaccination has all but eliminated the disease from most countries around the world. An iron-lung ward, such as the one shown in this 1953 photograph, housed patients paralyzed from polio and unable to breathe for themselves.

People living in developed nations and born in the 1960s or later may have difficulty understanding the once heavy burden of devastating infectious diseases. For example, smallpox, a deadly viral disease, once destroyed entire civilizations but has since been eradicated. Thanks to the vaccination efforts by multiple groups, including the World Health Organization, Rotary International, and the United Nations Children's Fund (UNICEF), smallpox has not been diagnosed in a patient since 1977. Polio is another excellent example. This crippling viral disease paralyzed patients, who were often kept alive in "iron lung wards" as recently as the 1950s . Today, vaccination against polio has nearly eradicated the disease. Vaccines have also reduced the prevalence of once-common infectious diseases such as chickenpox, German measles, measles, mumps, and whooping cough.

Overview Adaptive Immunity

Adaptive immunity is defined by two important characteristics: specificity and memory. Specificity refers to the adaptive immune system's ability to target specific pathogens, and memory refers to its ability to quickly respond to pathogens to which it has previously been exposed. For example, when an individual recovers from chickenpox, the body develops a *memory* of the infection that will *specifically* protect it from the causative agent, the varicella-zoster virus, if it is exposed to the virus again later.

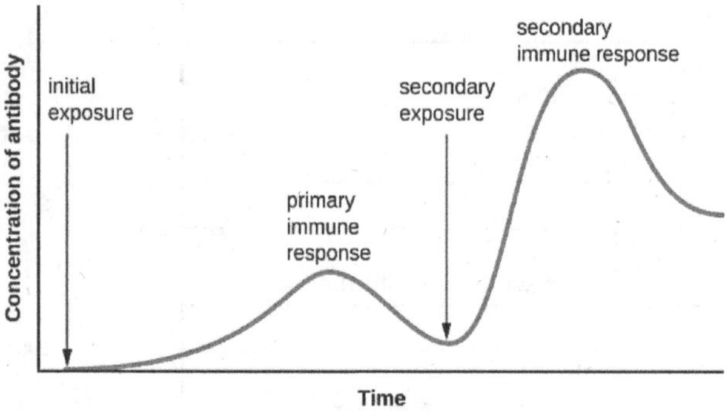

Specificity and memory are achieved by essentially programming certain cells involved in the immune response to respond rapidly to subsequent exposures of the pathogen. This programming occurs as a result of the first exposure to a pathogen or vaccine, which triggers a **primary response**. Subsequent exposures result in a secondary response that is faster and stronger as a result of the body's memory of the first exposure . This **secondary response**, however, is specific to the pathogen in question. For example, exposure to one virus (e.g., varicella-zoster virus) will not provide protection against other viral diseases (e.g., measles, mumps, or polio).

Figure 2 This graph illustrates the primary and secondary immune responses related to antibody production after an initial and secondary exposure to an antigen. Notice that the secondary response is faster and provides a much higher concentration of antibody.

Antigens

Activation of the adaptive immune defenses is triggered by pathogen-specific molecular structures called antigens.

The term ***antigen*** was initially used to describe molecules that stimulate the production of antibodies; in fact, the term comes from a combination of the words <u>anti</u>body and <u>gen</u>erator, and a molecule that stimulates antibody production is said to be antigenic.

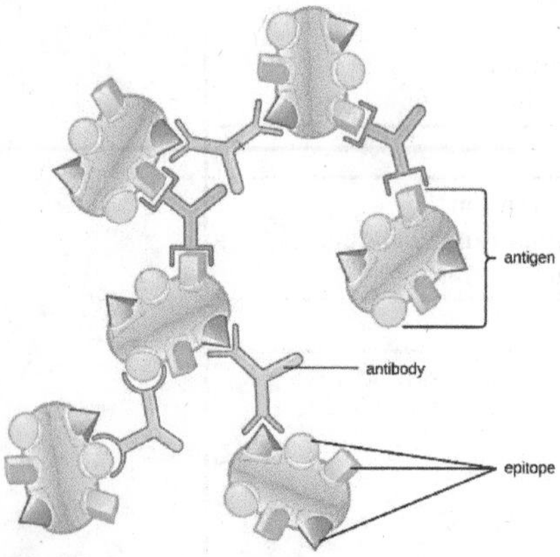

Pathogens possess a variety of structures that may contain antigens. For example, antigens from bacterial cells may be associated with their capsules, cell walls, fimbriae, flagella, or pili. Bacterial antigens may also be associated with extracellular toxins and enzymes that they secrete. Viruses possess a variety of antigens associated with their capsids, envelopes, and the spike structures they use for attachment to cells.

Antibodies

Antibodies (also called immunoglobulins) are glycoproteins that are present in both the blood and tissue fluids. They are typically "Y" shaped with the two top parts of the Y being binding regions for specific antigens.

Figure 3 A typical protein antigen has multiple epitopes, shown by the ability of three different antibodies to bind to different epitopes of the same antigen.

Vaccines

For many diseases, prevention is the best form of treatment, and few strategies for disease prevention are as effective as vaccination. Vaccination is a form of artificial immunity. By artificially stimulating the adaptive immune defenses, a vaccine triggers memory cell production similar to that which would occur during a primary response. In so doing, the patient is able to mount a strong secondary response upon exposure to the pathogen—but without having to first suffer through an initial infection. In this section, we will explore several different kinds of artificial immunity along with various types of vaccines and the mechanisms by which they induce artificial immunity.

Herd Immunity (Community Immunity)

Any given population is likely to have some individuals who are immune and other individuals who are susceptible to a specific disease. If a population has very few susceptible individuals, even those susceptible individuals will be protected by a phenomenon called **herd immunity** (or **community immunity**). Herd immunity has nothing to do with an individual's ability to mount an effective immune response; rather, it occurs because there are too few susceptible individuals in a population for the disease to spread effectively.

Vaccination programs create herd immunity by greatly reducing the number of susceptible individuals in a population. Even if some individuals in the population are not vaccinated, as long as a certain percentage is immune (either naturally or artificially), the few susceptible individuals are unlikely to be exposed to the pathogen. However, because new individuals are constantly entering populations (for example, through birth or relocation), vaccination programs are necessary to maintain herd immunity.

Variolation and Vaccination

Figure 4 *Variolation for smallpox origi-nated in the Far East and the practice later spread to Europe and Africa. This Japanese relief depicts a patient receiving a smallpox variolation from the physician Ogata Shun-saku (1748–1810).*

Thousands of years ago, it was first recognized that individuals who survived a smallpox infection were immune to subsequent infections. The practice of inoculating individuals to actively protect them from smallpox appears to have originated in the 10th century in China, when the practice of **variolation** was described. Variolation refers to the deliberate inoculation of individuals with infectious material from scabs or pustules of smallpox victims. Infectious materials were either injected into the skin or introduced through the nasal route. The infection that developed was usually milder than naturally acquired smallpox, and recovery from the milder infection provided protection against the more serious disease.

Although the majority of individuals treated by variolation developed only mild infections, the practice was not without risks. More serious and sometimes fatal infections did occur, and because smallpox was contagious, infections resulting from variolation could lead to epidemics. Even so, the practice of variolation for smallpox prevention spread to other regions, including India, Africa, and Europe.

Although variolation had been practiced for centuries, the English physician **Edward Jenner** (1749–1823) is generally credited with developing the modern process of vaccination. Jenner observed that milkmaids who developed cowpox, a disease similar to smallpox but milder, were immune to the more serious smallpox. This led Jenner to hypothesize that exposure to a less virulent pathogen could provide immune protection against a more virulent pathogen, providing a safer alternative to variolation. In 1796, Jenner tested his hypothesis by obtaining infectious samples from a milkmaid's active cowpox lesion and injecting the materials into a young boy. The boy developed a mild infection that included a low-grade fever, discomfort in his axillae (armpit) and loss of appetite. When the boy was later infected with infectious samples from smallpox lesions, he did not contract smallpox.[4] This new approach was termed **vaccination**, a name deriving from the use of cowpox (Latin *vacca* meaning "cow") to protect against smallpox. Today, we know that Jenner's vaccine worked because the cowpox virus is genetically and antigenically related to the *Variola* viruses that caused smallpox. Exposure to cowpox antigens resulted in a primary response and the production of memory cells that identical or related epitopes of Variola virus upon a later exposure to smallpox.

The success of Jenner's smallpox vaccination led other scientists to develop vaccines for other diseases. Perhaps the most notable was Louis Pasteur, who developed vaccines for rabies, cholera, and anthrax. During the 20th and 21st centuries, effective vaccines were developed to prevent a wide range of diseases caused by viruses (e.g., chickenpox and shingles, hepatitis, measles, mumps, polio, and yellow fever) and bacteria (e.g., diphtheria, pneumococcal pneumonia, tetanus, and whooping cough,).

(a)

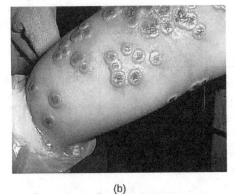

(b)

Figure 5 *(a) A painting of Edward Jenner depicts a cow and a milkmaid in the background. (b) Lesions on a patient infected with cowpox, a zoonotic disease caused by a virus closely related to the one that causes smallpox. (credit b: modification of work by the Centers for Disease Control and Prevention)*

Classes of Vaccines

For a vaccine to provide protection against a disease, it must expose an individual to pathogen-specific antigens that will stimulate a protective adaptive immune response. By its very nature, this entails some risk. As with any pharmaceutical drug, vaccines have the potential to cause adverse effects. However, the ideal vaccine causes no severe adverse effects and poses no risk of contracting the disease that it is intended to prevent. Various types of vaccines have been developed with these goals in mind.

Live attenuated vaccines expose an individual to a weakened strain of a pathogen with the goal of establishing a subclinical infection that will activate the adaptive immune defenses. Pathogens are attenuated to decrease their virulence using methods such as genetic manipulation (to eliminate key virulence factors) or long-term culturing in an unnatural host or environment (to promote mutations and decrease virulence).

By establishing an active infection, live attenuated vaccines stimulate a more comprehensive immune response than some other types of vaccines. Live attenuated vaccines activate both cellular and humoral immunity and stimulate the development of memory for long-lasting immunity. In some cases, vaccination of one individual with a live attenuated pathogen can even lead to natural transmission of the attenuated pathogen to other individuals. This can cause the other individuals to also develop an active, subclinical infection that activates their adaptive immune defenses.

Disadvantages associated with live attenuated vaccines include the challenges associated with long-term storage and transport as well as the potential for a patient to develop signs and symptoms of disease during the active infection (particularly in immunocompromised patients). There is also a risk of the attenuated pathogen reverting back to full virulence.

Inactivated vaccines contain whole pathogens that have been killed or inactivated with heat, chemicals, or radiation. For inactivated vaccines to be effective, the inactivation process must not affect the structure of key antigens on the pathogen.

Because the pathogen is killed or inactive, inactivated vaccines do not produce an active infection, and the resulting immune response is weaker and less comprehensive than that provoked by a live attenuated vaccine. Typically the response involves only humoral immunity, and the pathogen cannot be transmitted to other individuals. In addition, inactivated vaccines usually require higher doses and multiple boosters, possibly causing inflammatory reactions at the site of injection.

Despite these disadvantages, inactivated vaccines do have the advantages of long-term storage stability and ease of transport. Also, there is no risk of causing severe active infections. However, inactivated vaccines are not without their side effects.

Whereas live attenuated and inactive vaccines expose an individual to a weakened or dead pathogen, **subunit vaccines** only expose the patient to the key antigens of a pathogen—not whole cells or viruses. Subunit vaccines can be produced either by chemically degrading a pathogen and isolating its key antigens or by producing the antigens through genetic engineering. Because these vaccines contain only the essential antigens of a pathogen, the risk of side effects is relatively low.

Like subunit vaccines, **toxoid vaccines** do not introduce a whole pathogen to the patient; they contain inactivated bacterial toxins, called toxoids. Toxoid vaccines are used to prevent diseases in which bacterial toxins play an important role in pathogenesis. These vaccines activate humoral immunity that neutralizes the toxins.

Classes of Vaccines				
Class	**Description**	**Advantages**	**Disadvantages**	**Examples**
Live attenuated	Weakened strain of whole pathogen	Cellular and humoral immunity	Difficult to store and transport	Chickenpox, German measles, measles, mumps, tuberculosis, typhoid fever, yellow fever
		Long-lasting immunity	Risk of infection in immunocompromised patients	
		Transmission to contacts	Risk of reversion	
Inactivated	Whole pathogen killed or inactivated with heat, chemicals, or radiation	Ease of storage and transport	Weaker immunity (humoral only)	Cholera, hepatitis A, influenza, plague, rabies
		No risk of severe active infection	Higher doses and more boosters required	
Subunit	Immunogenic antigens	Lower risk of side effects	Limited longevity	Anthrax, hepatitis B, influenza, meningitis, papillomavirus, pneumococcal pneumonia, whooping cough
			Multiple doses required	
			No protection against antigenic variation	
Toxoid	Inactivated bacterial toxin	Humoral immunity to neutralize toxin	Does not prevent infection	Botulism, diphtheria, pertussis, tetanus

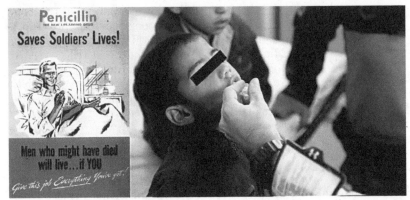

History of Chemotherapy and Antimicrobial Discovery

Most people associate the term chemotherapy with treatments for cancer. However, chemotherapy is actually a broader term that refers to any use of chemicals or drugs to treat disease. Chemotherapy may involve drugs that target cancerous cells or tissues, or it may involve **antimicrobial drugs** that target infectious microorganisms. Antimicrobial drugs typically work by destroying or interfering with microbial structures and enzymes, either killing microbial cells or inhibiting of their growth. But before we examine how these drugs work, we will briefly explore the history of humans' use of antimicrobials for the purpose of chemotherapy.

The First Antimicrobial Drugs

Figure 6 First mass produced in the 1940s, penicillin was instrumental in saving millions of lives during World War II and was considered a wonder drug.[1] Today, over prescription of antibiotics (especially for childhood illnesses) has contributed to the evolution of drug-resistant pathogens. (credit left: modification of work by Chemical Heritage Foundation; credit right: modification of work by U.S. Department of Defense)

Societies relied on traditional medicine for thousands of years; however, the first half of the 20th century brought an era of strategic drug discovery. In the early 1900s, the German physician and scientist **Paul Ehrlich** (1854–1915) set out to discover or synthesize chemical compounds capable of killing infectious microbes without harming the patient. In 1909, after screening more than 600 arsenic-containing compounds, Ehrlich's assistant Sahachiro Hata (1873–1938) found one such "**magic bullet**." Compound 606 targeted the bacterium *Treponema pallidum*, the causative agent of syphilis. Compound 606 was found to successfully cure syphilis in rabbits and soon after was marketed under the name **Salvarsan** as a remedy for the disease in humans. Ehrlich's innovative approach of systematically screening a wide variety of compounds remains a common strategy for the discovery of new antimicrobial agents even today.

Figure 7 Paul Ehrlich was influential in the discovery of Compound 606, an antimicrobial agent that proved to be an effective treatment for syphilis.

A few decades later, German scientists Josef Klarer, Fritz Mietzsch, and Gerhard Domagk discovered the antibacterial activity of a synthetic dye, prontosil, that could treat streptococcal and staphylococcal infections in mice. Domagk's own daughter was one of the first human recipients of the drug, which completely cured her of a severe streptococcal infection that had resulted from a poke with an embroidery needle. Gerhard Domagk (1895–1964) was awarded the Nobel Prize in Medicine in 1939 for his work with prontosil and sulfanilamide, the active breakdown product of prontosil in the body. Sulfanilamide, the first synthetic antimicrobial created, served as the foundation for the chemical development of a family of sulfa drugs. A **synthetic antimicrobial** is a drug that is developed from a chemical not found in nature. The success of the sulfa drugs led to the discovery and production of additional important classes of synthetic antimicrobials, including the quinolines and oxazolidinones.

Fundamentals of Antimicrobial Chemotherapy

Several factors are important in choosing the most appropriate antimicrobial drug therapy, including bacteriostatic versus bactericidal mechanisms, spectrum of activity, dosage and route of administration, the potential for side effects, and the potential interactions between drugs. The following discussion will focus primarily on antibacterial drugs, but the concepts translate to other antimicrobial classes.

Bacteriostatic Versus Bactericidal

Antibacterial drugs can be either bacteriostatic or bactericidal in their interactions with target bacteria. **Bacteriostatic** drugs cause a reversible inhibition of growth, with bacterial growth restarting after elimination of the drug. By contrast, bactericidal drugs kill their target bacteria. The decision of whether to use a bacteriostatic or **bactericidal** drugs depends on the type of infection and the immune status of the patient. In a patient with strong immune defenses, bacteriostatic and bactericidal drugs can be effective in achieving clinical cure. However, when a patient is immunocompromised, a bactericidal drug is essential for the successful treatment of infections. Regardless of the immune status of the patient, life-threatening infections such as acute endocarditis require the use of a bactericidal drug.

Spectrum of Activity

The **spectrum of activity** of an antibacterial drug relates to diversity of targeted bacteria. A **narrow-spectrum antimicrobial** targets only specific subsets of bacterial pathogens. For example, some narrow-spectrum drugs only target gram-positive bacteria, whereas others target only gram-negative bacteria. If the pathogen causing an infection has been identified, it is best to use a narrow-spectrum antimicrobial and minimize collateral damage to the normal microbiota. A **broad-spectrum antimicrobial** targets a wide variety of bacterial pathogens, including both gram-positive and gram-negative species, and is frequently used as empiric therapy to cover a wide

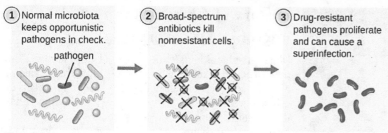

(1) Normal microbiota keeps opportunistic pathogens in check.
pathogen

(2) Broad-spectrum antibiotics kill nonresistant cells.

(3) Drug-resistant pathogens proliferate and can cause a superinfection.

Figure 8 Broad-spectrum antimicrobial use may lead to the development of a superinfection. (credit: modification of work by Centers for Disease Control and Prevention)

range of potential pathogens while waiting on the laboratory identification of the infecting pathogen. Broad-spectrum antimicrobials are also used for polymicrobic infections (mixed infection with multiple bacterial species), or as prophylactic prevention of infections with surgery/invasive procedures. Finally, broad-spectrum antimicrobials may be selected to treat an infection when a narrow-spectrum drug fails because of development of drug resistance by the target pathogen.

The risk associated with using broad-spectrum antimicrobials is that they will also target a broad spectrum of the normal microbiota, increasing the risk of a **superinfection,** a secondary infection in a patient having a preexisting infection. A superinfection develops when the antibacterial intended for the preexisting infection kills the protective microbiota, allowing another pathogen resistant to the antibacterial to proliferate and cause a secondary infection. Common examples of superinfections that develop as a result of antimicrobial usage include yeast infections (candidiasis) and pseudomembranous colitis caused by *Clostridium difficile*, which can be fatal.

Mechanisms of Antimicrobial Drugs

An important quality for an antimicrobial drug is **selective toxicity**, meaning that it selectively kills or inhibits the growth of microbial targets while causing minimal or no harm to the host. Most antimicrobial drugs currently in clinical use are antibacterial because the prokaryotic cell provides a greater variety of unique targets for selective toxicity, in comparison to fungi, parasites, and viruses. Each class of antibacterial drugs has a unique **mode of action** (the way in which a drug affects microbes at the cellular level).

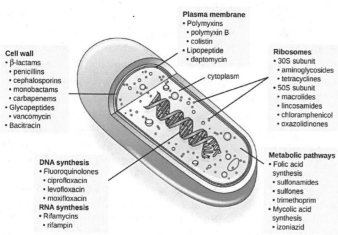

Because fungi, protozoa, and helminths are eukaryotic, their cells are very similar to human cells, making it more difficult to develop drugs with selective toxicity. Additionally, viruses replicate within human host cells, making it difficult to develop drugs that are selectively toxic to viruses or virus-infected cells. Despite these challenges, there are antimicrobial drugs that target fungi, protozoa, helminths, and viruses, and some even target more than one type of microbe.

Figure 9 There are several classes of antibacterial compounds that are typically classified based on their bacterial target.

Drug Resistance

Antimicrobial resistance is not a new phenomenon. In nature, microbes are constantly evolving in order to overcome the antimicrobial compounds produced by other microorganisms. Human development of antimicrobial drugs and their widespread clinical use has simply provided another selective pressure that promotes further evolution. Several important factors can accelerate the evolution of **drug resistance**. These include the overuse and misuse of antimicrobials, inappropriate use of antimicrobials, subtherapeutic dosing, and patient noncompliance with the recommended course of treatment.

Exposure of a pathogen to an antimicrobial compound can select for chromosomal mutations conferring resistance, which can be transferred vertically to subsequent microbial generations and eventually become predominant in a microbial population that is repeatedly exposed to the antimicrobial. Alternatively, many genes responsible for drug resistance are found on plasmids or in transposons that can be transferred easily between microbes through horizontal gene transfer.

From a clinical perspective, our greatest concerns are **multidrug-resistant microbes (MDRs)**. MDRs are colloquially known as "superbugs" and carry one or more resistance mechanism(s), making them resistant to multiple antimicrobials. In recent years, several clinically important superbugs have emerged, and the CDC reports that superbugs are responsible for more than 2 million infections in the US annually, resulting in at least 23,000 fatalities. Several of the superbugs discussed in the following sections have been dubbed the ESKAPE pathogens. This acronym refers to the names of the pathogens (*Enterococcus faecium, Staphylococcus aureus, Klebsiella pneumoniae, Acinetobacter baumannii, Pseudomonas aeruginosa* and *Enterobacter* spp.) but it is also fitting in that these pathogens are able to "escape" many conventional forms of antimicrobial therapy. As such, infections by ESKAPE pathogens can be difficult to treat and they cause a large number of nosocomial infections.

Staphylococcal Infections and MRSA

Staphylococcus species are commonly found on the skin, with *S. epidermidis* and *S. hominis* being prevalent in the normal microbiota. *S. aureus* is also commonly found in the nasal passages and on healthy skin, but pathogenic strains are often the cause of a broad range of infections of the skin and other body systems.

S. *aureus* is quite contagious. It is spread easily through skin-to-skin contact, and because many people are chronic nasal carriers (asymptomatic individuals who carry *S. aureus* in their nares), the bacteria can easily be transferred from the nose to the hands and then to fomites or other individuals. Because it is so contagious, *S. aureus* is prevalent in most community settings. This prevalence is particularly problematic in hospitals, where antibiotic-resistant strains of the bacteria may be present, and where immunocompromised patients may be more susceptible to infection. Resistant strains include **methicillin-resistant *S. aureus* (MRSA)**, which can be acquired through health-care settings (hospital-acquired MRSA, or **HA-MRSA**) or in the community (community-acquired MRSA, or **CA-MRSA**). Hospital patients often arrive at health-care facilities already colonized with antibiotic-resistant strains of *S. aureus* that can be transferred to health-care providers and other patients. Some hospitals have attempted to detect these individuals in order to institute prophylactic measures, but they have had mixed success.

S. *aureus* is distinguished from less pathogenic staphylococci like *S. epidermidis* by culturing the sample on mannitol salt agar (MSA). *Staphylococcus* species readily grow on this medium because they are tolerant of the high concentration of sodium chloride (7.5% NaCl). However, *S. aureus* ferment mannitol (which will be evident on a MSA plate), *S. epidermidis* do not ferment mannitol. Fermentation of mannitol will cause MSA to turn from red to yellow when growing *S. aureus*. A positive coagulase test can further confirm the identity of *S. aureus*. Although coagulase negative species like *S. epidermidis* are less likely to cause human disease, they can cause infections

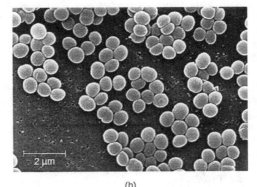

when they enter the body, as can sometimes occur via catheters, indwelling medical devices, and wounds.

Superficial Staphylococcal Infections

S. *aureus* is often associated with pyoderma, skin infections that are purulent. Pus formation occurs because many strains of *S. aureus* produce leukocidins, which kill white blood cells. These purulent skin infections may initially manifest as folliculitis, but can lead to furuncles or deeper abscesses called carbuncles.

Folliculitis generally presents as bumps and pimples that may be itchy, red, and/or pus-filled. In some cases, folliculitis is self-limiting, but if it continues for more than a few days, worsens, or returns repeatedly, it may require medical treatment. Sweat, skin injuries, ingrown hairs, tight clothing, irritation from shaving, and skin conditions can all contribute

Figure 10 *(a) A mannitol salt agar plate is used to distinguish different species of staphylococci. In this plate, S. aureus is on the left and S. epidermidis is in the right. Because S. aureus is capable of fermenting mannitol, it produces acids that cause the color to change to yellow. (b) This scanning electron micrograph shows the characteristic grapelike clusters of S. aureus. (credit a: modification of work by "ScienceProfOnline"/YouTube; credit b: modification of work by Centers for Disease Control and Prevention)*

to folliculitis. Avoidance of tight clothing and skin irritation can help to prevent infection, but topical antibiotics (and sometimes other treatments) may also help. Folliculitis can be identified by skin inspection; treatment is generally started without first culturing and identifying the causative agent.

In contrast, furuncles (boils) are deeper infections. They are most common in those individuals (especially young adults and teenagers) who play contact sports, share athletic equipment, have poor nutrition, live in close quarters, or have weakened immune systems. Good hygiene and skin care can often help to prevent furuncles from becoming more infective, and they generally resolve on their own. However, if furuncles spread, increase in number or size, or lead to systemic symptoms such as fever and chills, then medical care is needed. They may sometimes need to be drained (at which time the pathogens can be cultured) and treated with antibiotics.

When multiple boils develop into a deeper lesion, it is called a carbuncle. Because carbuncles are deeper, they are more commonly associated with systemic symptoms and a general feeling of illness. Larger, recurrent, or worsening carbuncles require medical treatment,

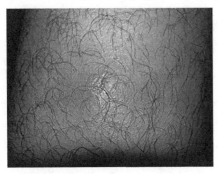 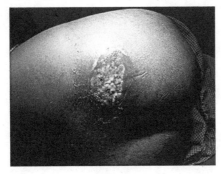

as do those associated with signs of illness such as fever. Carbuncles generally need to be drained and treated with antibiotics. While carbuncles are relatively easy to identify visually, culturing and laboratory analysis of the wound may be recommended for some infections because antibiotic resistance is relatively common.

Proper hygiene is important to prevent these types of skin infections or to prevent the progression of existing infections.

The skin infection **impetigo** causes the formation of vesicles, pustules, and possibly bullae, often around the nose and mouth. Bullae are large, fluid-filled blisters that measure at least 5 mm in diameter. Impetigo can be diagnosed as either nonbullous or bullous. In nonbullous

Figure 11 *Furuncles (boils) and carbuncles are infections of the skin often caused by Staphylococcus bacteria. (a) A furuncle contains pus and exhibits swelling. (b) A carbuncle is a pus-filled lesion that is typically deeper than the furuncle. It often forms from multiple furuncles. (credit a: modification of work by "Mahdouch"/Wikimedia Commons; credit b: modification of work by "Drvgaikwad"/Wikimedia Commons)*

impetigo, vesicles and pustules rupture and become encrusted sores. Typically the crust is yellowish, often with exudate draining from the base of the lesion. In bullous impetigo, the bullae fill and rupture, resulting in larger, draining, encrusted lesions.

Especially common in children, impetigo is particularly concerning because it is highly contagious. Impetigo can be caused by *S. aureus* alone, by *Streptococcus pyogenes* alone, or by coinfection of *S. aureus* and *S. pyogenes*. Impetigo is often diagnosed through observation of its characteristic appearance, although culture and susceptibility testing may also be used.

Topical or oral antibiotic treatment is typically effective in treating most cases of impetigo. However, cases caused by *S. pyogenes* can lead to serious sequelae (pathological conditions resulting from infection, disease, injury, therapy, or other trauma) such as acute glomerulonephritis (AGN), which is severe inflammation in the kidneys.

Vancomycin-Resistant Enterococci and *Staphylococcus aureus*

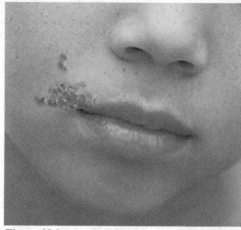

Figure 12 *Impetigo is characterized by vesicles, pustules, or bullae that rupture, producing encrusted sores. (credit: modification of work by FDA)*

Vancomycin is only effective against gram-positive organisms, and it is used to treat wound infections, septic infections, endocarditis, and meningitis that are caused by pathogens resistant to other antibiotics. It is considered one of the last lines of defense against such resistant infections, including MRSA. With the rise of antibiotic resistance in the 1970s and 1980s, vancomycin use increased, and it is not surprising that we saw the emergence and spread of **vancomycin-resistant enterococci (VRE),** vancomycin-resistant *S. aureus* (VRSA), and vancomycin-intermediate *S. aureus* (VISA). The mechanism of vancomycin resistance among enterococci is target modification involving a structural change to the peptide component of the peptidoglycan subunits, preventing vancomycin from binding. These strains are typically spread among patients in clinical settings by contact with health-care workers and contaminated surfaces and medical equipment.

Multidrug-Resistant *Mycobacterium tuberculosis*

The emergence of **multidrug-resistant *Mycobacterium tuberculosis* (MDR-TB)** and **extensively drug-resistant *Mycobacterium tuberculosis* (XDR-TB)** is also of significant global concern. MDR-TB strains are resistant to both rifampin and isoniazid, the drug combination typically prescribed for treatment of tuberculosis. XDR-TB strains are additionally resistant to any fluoroquinolone and at least one of three other drugs (amikacin, kanamycin, or capreomycin) used as a second line of treatment, leaving these patients very few treatment options. Both types of pathogens are particularly problematic in immunocompromised persons, including those suffering from HIV infection. The development of resistance in these strains often results from the incorrect use of antimicrobials for tuberculosis treatment, selecting for resistance.

Infectious Disease

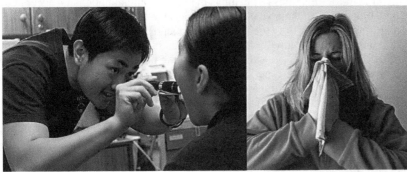

Jane woke up one spring morning feeling not quite herself. Her throat felt a bit dry and she was sniffling. She wondered why she felt so lousy. Was it because of a change in the weather? The pollen count? Was she coming down with something? Did she catch a bug from her coworker who sneezed on her in the elevator yesterday?

The signs and symptoms we associate with illness can have many different causes. Sometimes they are the direct result of a pathogenic infection, but in other cases they result from a response by our immune system to a pathogen or another perceived threat. For example, in response to certain pathogens, the immune system may release pyrogens, chemicals that cause the body temperature to rise, resulting in a fever. This response

Figure 1 *Although medical professionals rely heavily on signs and symptoms to diagnose disease and prescribe treatment, many diseases can produce similar signs and symptoms. (credit left: modification of work by U.S. Navy)*

creates a less-than-favorable environment for the pathogen, but it also makes us feel sick.

Medical professionals rely heavily on analysis of signs and symptoms to determine the cause of an ailment and prescribe treatment. In some cases, signs and symptoms alone are enough to correctly identify the causative agent of a disease, but since few diseases produce truly unique symptoms, it is often necessary to confirm the identity of the infectious agent by other direct and indirect diagnostic methods.

Characteristics of Infectious Disease

A **disease** is any condition in which the normal structure or functions of the body are damaged or impaired. Physical injuries or disabilities are not classified as disease, but there can be several causes for disease, including infection by a pathogen, genetics (as in many cancers or deficiencies), noninfectious environmental causes, or inappropriate immune responses. Our focus in this chapter will be on **infectious diseases**, although when diagnosing infectious diseases, it is always important to consider possible noninfectious causes.

An **infection** is the successful colonization of a host by a microorganism or **causative agent**. Infections can lead to disease, which causes signs and symptoms resulting in a deviation from the normal structure or functioning of the host. Microorganisms that can cause disease are known as **pathogens**.

Signs and Symptoms of Disease

The **sign**s of disease are objective and measurable, and can be directly observed by a clinician. Vital signs, which are used to measure the body's basic functions, include body temperature (normally 37 °C [98.6 °F]), heart rate (normally 60–100 beats per minute), breathing rate (normally 12–18 breaths per minute), and blood pressure (normally between 90/60 and 120/80 mm Hg). Changes in any of the body's vital signs may be indicative of disease. For example, having a fever (a body temperature significantly higher than 37 °C or 98.6 °F) is a sign of disease because it can be measured.

In addition to changes in vital signs, other observable conditions may be considered signs of disease. For example, the presence of antibodies in a patient's serum (the liquid portion of blood that lacks clotting factors) can be observed and measured through blood tests and, therefore, can be considered a sign. However, it is important to note that the presence of antibodies is not always a sign of an active disease. Antibodies can remain in the body long after an infection has resolved; also, they may develop in response to a pathogen that is in the body but not currently causing disease.

Unlike signs, **symptom**s of disease are subjective. Symptoms are felt or experienced by the patient, but they cannot be clinically confirmed or objectively measured. Examples of symptoms include nausea, loss of appetite, and pain. Such symptoms are important to consider when diagnosing disease, but they are subject to memory bias and are difficult to measure precisely. Some clinicians attempt to quantify symptoms by asking patients to assign a numerical value to their symptoms. For example, the Wong-Baker Faces pain-rating scale asks patients to rate their pain on a scale of 0–10. An alternative method of quantifying pain is measuring skin conductance fluctuations. These fluctuations reflect sweating due to skin sympathetic nerve activity resulting from the stressor of pain.

Clinicians must rely on signs and on asking questions about symptoms, medical history, and the patient's recent activities to identify a particular disease and the potential causative agent. Diagnosis is complicated by the fact that different microorganisms can cause similar signs and symptoms in a patient. For example, an individual presenting with symptoms of diarrhea may have been infected by one of a wide variety of pathogenic microorganisms. Bacterial pathogens associated with diarrheal disease include *Vibrio cholerae*, *Listeria monocytogenes*, *Campylobacter jejuni*, and enteropathogenic *Escherichia coli* (EPEC). Viral pathogens associated with diarrheal disease include norovirus and rotavirus. Parasitic pathogens associated with diarrhea include *Giardia lamblia* and *Cryptosporidium parvum*. Likewise, fever is indicative of many types of infection, from the common cold to the deadly Ebola hemorrhagic fever.

Finally, some diseases may be asymptomatic or subclinical, meaning they do not present any noticeable signs or symptoms. For example, most individual infected with herpes simplex virus remain asymptomatic and are unaware that they have been infected.

Some Diseases are Named by the Location of the Disease - Pneumonia

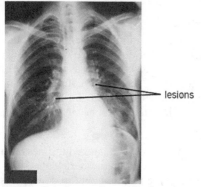

Figure 2 *A chest radiograph of a patient with pneumonia shows the consolidations (lesions) present as opaque patches. (credit: modification of work by Centers for Disease Control and Prevention)*

Pneumonia is a general term for infections of the lungs that lead to inflammation and accumulation of fluids and white blood cells in the alveoli. Pneumonia can be caused by bacteria, viruses, fungi, and other organisms, although the vast majority of pneumonias are bacterial in origin. Bacterial pneumonia is a prevalent, potentially serious infection; it caused more 50,000 deaths in the United States in 2014. As the alveoli fill with fluids and white blood cells (consolidation), air exchange becomes impaired and patients experience respiratory distress. In addition, pneumonia can lead to pleurisy, an infection of the pleural membrane surrounding the lungs, which can make breathing very painful. Although many different bacteria can cause pneumonia under the right circumstances, three bacterial species cause most clinical cases: *Streptococcus pneumoniae*, *H. influenzae*, and *Mycoplasma pneumoniae*. In addition to these, we will also examine some of the less common causes of pneumonia.

The most common cause of community-acquired bacterial pneumonia is *Streptococcus pneumonia* and is referred to as **pneumococcal pneumonia**. The pneumococci initially colonize the bronchioles of the lungs. Eventually, the infection spreads to the alveoli. The resulting inflammatory response causes the alveoli to fill with exudate rich in neutrophils and red blood cells. As a consequence, infected individuals develop a productive cough with bloody sputum.

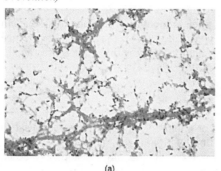

(a)

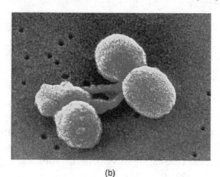

(b)

Figure 3 *(a) This micrograph of Streptococcus pneumoniae grown from a blood culture shows the characteristic lancet-shaped diplococcal morphology. (b) A colorized scanning electron micrograph of S. pneumoniae. (credit a: modification of work by Centers for Disease Control and Prevention; credit b: modification of work by Janice Carr, Centers for Disease Control and Prevention)*

Primary atypical pneumonia is caused by *Mycoplasma pneumoniae*. This bacterium is not part of the respiratory tract's normal microbiota and can cause epidemic disease outbreaks. Also known as **walking pneumonia,** *mycoplasma* pneumonia infections are common in crowded environments like college campuses and military bases. It is spread by aerosols formed when coughing or sneezing. The disease is often mild, with a low fever and persistent cough. Mycoplasma grow very slowly when cultured.

A variety of opportunistic bacteria that do not typically cause respiratory disease in healthy individuals are common causes of health care-associated pneumonia. These include *Klebsiella pneumoniae*, *Staphylococcus aureus*, and proteobacteria such as species of *Escherichia*, *Proteus*, and *Serratia*. Patients at risk include the elderly, those who have other preexisting lung conditions, and those who are immunocompromised. In addition, patients receiving supportive therapies such as intubation, antibiotics, and immunomodulatory drugs may also be at risk because these interventions disrupt the mucociliary escalator and other pulmonary defenses. Invasive medical devices such as catheters, medical implants, and ventilators can also introduce opportunistic pneumonia-causing pathogens into the body.

Pseudomonas aeruginosa is another opportunistic pathogen that can cause serious cases of bacterial pneumonia in patients with cystic fibrosis (CF) and hospitalized patients assisted with artificial ventilators. This bacterium is extremely antibiotic resistant and can produce a variety of exotoxins. Ventilator-associated pneumonia with *P. aeruginosa* is caused by contaminated equipment that causes the pathogen to be aspirated into the lungs. In patients with CF, a genetic defect in the cystic fibrosis transmembrane receptor (CFTR) leads to the accumulation of excess dried mucus in the lungs. Lung damage from the chronic inflammatory response that ensues is the leading cause of mortality in patients with CF.

Viruses cause fewer cases of pneumonia than bacteria; however, several viruses can lead to pneumonia in children and the elderly. The most common sources of viral pneumonia are adenoviruses, influenza viruses, parainfluenza viruses, and respiratory syncytial viruses. The signs and symptoms produced by these viruses can range from mild cold-like symptoms to severe cases of pneumonia, depending on the virulence of the virus strain and the strength of the host defenses of the infected individual. Occasionally, infections can result in otitis media.

General Characteristics of Pathogens

Pathogenicity and Virulence

The ability of a microbial agent to cause disease is called **pathogenicity**, and the degree to which an organism is pathogenic is called **virulence**. Virulence is a continuum. On one end of the spectrum are organisms that are avirulent (not harmful) and on the other are organisms that are highly virulent. Highly virulent pathogens will almost always lead to a disease state when introduced to the body, and some may even cause multi-organ and body system failure in healthy individuals. Less virulent pathogens may cause an initial infection, but may not always cause severe illness. Pathogens with low virulence would more likely result in mild signs and symptoms of disease, such as low-grade fever, headache, or muscle aches. Some individuals might even be asymptomatic.

An example of a highly virulent microorganism is *Bacillus anthracis*, the pathogen responsible for anthrax. *B. anthracis* can produce different forms of disease, depending on the route of transmission (e.g., cutaneous injection, inhalation, ingestion). The most serious form of anthrax is inhalation anthrax. After *B. anthracis* spores are inhaled, they germinate. An active infection develops and the bacteria release potent toxins that cause edema (fluid buildup in tissues), hypoxia (a condition preventing oxygen from reaching tissues), and necrosis (cell death and inflammation). Signs and symptoms of inhalation anthrax include high fever, difficulty breathing, vomiting and coughing up blood, and severe chest pains suggestive of a heart attack. With inhalation anthrax, the toxins and bacteria enter the bloodstream, which can lead to multi-organ failure and death of the patient. If a gene (or genes) involved in pathogenesis is inactivated, the bacteria become less virulent or nonpathogenic.

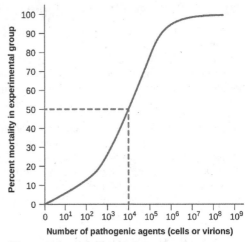

Figure 4 *A graph like this is used to determine LD_{50} by plotting pathogen concentration against the percent of infected test animals that have died. In this example, the $LD_{50} = 10^4$ pathogenic particles.*

Virulence of a pathogen can be quantified using controlled experiments with laboratory animals. Two important indicators of virulence are the **median infectious dose (ID_{50})** and the **median lethal dose (LD_{50})**, both of which are typically determined experimentally using animal models. The ID_{50} is the number of pathogen cells or virions required to cause active infection in 50% of inoculated animals. The LD_{50} is the number of pathogenic cells, virions, or amount of toxin required to kill 50% of infected animals. To calculate these values, each group of animals is inoculated with one of a range of known numbers of pathogen cells or virions. In graphs like the one shown in Figure 4, the percentage of animals that have been infected (for ID_{50}) or killed (for LD_{50}) is plotted against the concentration of pathogen inoculated. Figure 4 represents data graphed from a hypothetical experiment measuring the LD_{50} of a pathogen. Interpretation of the data from this graph indicates that the LD_{50} of the pathogen for the test animals is 10^4 pathogen cells or virions (depending upon the pathogen studied).

Table 1 lists selected foodborne pathogens and their ID_{50} values in humans (as determined from epidemiologic data and studies on human volunteers). Keep in mind that these are *median* values. The actual infective dose for an individual can vary widely, depending on factors such as route of entry; the age, health, and immune status of the host; and environmental and pathogen-specific factors such as susceptibility to the acidic pH of the stomach. It is also important to note that a pathogen's infective dose does not necessarily correlate with disease severity. For example, just a single cell of *Salmonella enterica* serotype Typhimurium can result in an active infection. The resultant disease, *Salmonella* gastroenteritis or salmonellosis, can cause nausea, vomiting, and diarrhea, but has a mortality rate of less than 1% in healthy adults. In contrast, *S. enterica* serotype Typhi has a much higher ID_{50}, typically requiring as many as 1,000 cells to produce infection. However, this serotype causes typhoid fever, a much more systemic and severe disease that has a mortality rate as high as 10% in untreated individuals.

ID_{50} for Selected Foodborne Diseases	
Pathogen	**ID_{50}**
Viruses	
Hepatitis A virus	10–100
Norovirus	1–10
Rotavirus	10–100
Bacteria	
Escherichia coli, enterohemorrhagic (EHEC, serotype O157)	10–100
E. coli, enteroinvasive (EIEC)	200–5,000
E. coli, enteropathogenic (EPEC)	10,000,000–10,000,000,000
E. coli, enterotoxigenic (ETEC)	10,000,000–10,000,000,000
Salmonella enterica serovar Typhi	<1,000
S. enterica serovar Typhimurium	≥1
Vibrio cholerae (serotypes O139, O1)	1,000,000
V. parahemolyticus	100,000,000
Protozoa	
Giardia lamblia	1
Cryptosporidium parvum	10–100

Table 1.

Primary Pathogens versus Opportunistic Pathogens

Pathogens can be classified as either primary pathogens or opportunistic pathogens. A **primary pathogen** can cause disease in a host regardless of the host's resident microbiota or immune system. An **opportunistic pathogen**, by contrast, can only cause disease in situations that compromise the host's defenses, such as the body's protective barriers, immune system, or normal microbiota. Individuals susceptible to opportunistic infections include the very young, the elderly, women who are pregnant, patients undergoing chemotherapy, people with immunodeficiencies (such as acquired immunodeficiency syndrome [AIDS]), patients who are recovering from surgery, and those who have had a breach of protective barriers (such as a severe wound or burn).

An example of a primary pathogen is enterohemorrhagic *E. coli* (EHEC), which produces a virulence factor known as Shiga toxin. This toxin inhibits protein synthesis, leading to severe and bloody diarrhea, inflammation, and renal failure, even in patients with healthy immune systems. *Staphylococcus epidermidis*, on the other hand, is an opportunistic pathogen that is among the most frequent causes of nosocomial disease. *S. epidermidis* is a member of the normal microbiota of the skin, where it is generally avirulent. However, in hospitals, it can also grow in biofilms that form on catheters, implants, or other devices that are inserted into the body during surgical procedures. Once inside the body, *S. epidermidis* can cause serious infections such as endocarditis, and it produces virulence factors that promote the persistence of such infections.

Other members of the normal microbiota can also cause opportunistic infections under certain conditions. This often occurs when microbes that reside harmlessly in one body location end up in a different body system, where they cause disease. For example, *E. coli* normally found in the large intestine can cause a urinary tract infection if it enters the bladder. This is the leading cause of urinary tract infections among women.

Members of the normal microbiota may also cause disease when a shift in the environment of the body leads to overgrowth of a particular microorganism. For example, the yeast *Candida* is part of the normal microbiota of the skin, mouth, intestine, and vagina, but its population is kept in check by other organisms of the microbiota. If an individual is taking antibacterial medications, however, bacteria that would normally inhibit the growth of *Candida* can be killed off, leading to a sudden growth in the population of *Candida*, which is not affected by antibacterial medications because it is a fungus. An overgrowth of *Candida* can manifest as **oral thrush** (growth on mouth, throat, and tongue), a vaginal yeast infection, or cutaneous candidiasis. Other scenarios can also provide opportunities for *Candida* infections. Untreated diabetes can result in a high concentration of glucose in the saliva, which provides an optimal environment for the growth of *Candida,* resulting in thrush. Immunodeficiencies such as those seen in patients with HIV, AIDS, and cancer also lead to higher incidence of thrush. Vaginal yeast infections can result from decreases in estrogen levels during the menstruation or menopause. The amount of glycogen available to lactobacilli in the vagina is controlled by levels of estrogen; when estrogen levels are low, lactobacilli produce less lactic acid. The resultant increase in vaginal pH allows overgrowth of *Candida* in the vagina.

Bacterial Virulence Factors

Some pathogens are more virulent than others. This is due to the unique **virulence factor**s produced by individual pathogens, which determine the extent and severity of disease they may cause. A pathogen's virulence factors are encoded by genes. Some pathogens produce extracellular enzymes, or **exoenzymes** (extracellular enzymes), that enable them to invade host cells and deeper tissues. Exoenzymes have a wide variety of targets. Each of these exoenzymes functions in the context of a particular tissue structure to facilitate invasion or support its own growth and defend against the immune system. For example, the exoenzyme **collagenase** digests collagen, the dominant protein in connective tissue. Collagen can be found in the extracellular matrix, especially near mucosal membranes, blood vessels, nerves, and in the layers of the skin. Similar collagenase allows the pathogen to penetrate and spread through the host tissue by digesting this connective tissue protein. The collagenase produced by the gram-positive bacterium *Clostridium perfringens*, for example, allows the bacterium to make its way through the tissue layers and subsequently enter and multiply in the blood (septicemia). *C. perfringens* then uses toxins and a phospholipase to cause cellular lysis and necrosis. Once the host cells have died, the bacterium produces gas by fermenting the muscle carbohydrates. The widespread necrosis of tissue and accompanying gas are characteristic of the condition known as **gas gangrene**.

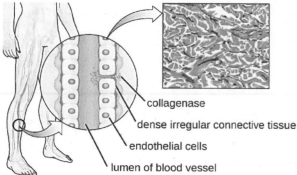

collagenase

dense irregular connective tissue

endothelial cells

lumen of blood vessel

Figure 5 *The illustration depicts a blood vessel with a single layer of endothelial cells surrounding the lumen and dense connective tissue (shown in red) surrounding the endothelial cell layer. Collagenase produced by C. perfringens degrades the collagen between the endothelial cells, allowing the bacteria to enter the bloodstream. (credit illustration: modification of work by Bruce Blaus; credit micrograph: Micrograph provided by the Regents of University of Michigan Medical School © 2012)*

Evading the immune system is also important to invasiveness. Bacteria use a variety of virulence factors to evade phagocytosis by cells of the immune system. For example, many bacteria produce **capsules**, which are used in adhesion but also aid in immune evasion by preventing ingestion by phagocytes. The composition of the capsule prevents immune cells from being able to adhere and then phagocytose the cell. In addition, the capsule makes the bacterial cell much larger, making it harder for immune cells to engulf the pathogen. A notable capsule-producing bacterium is the gram-positive pathogen *Streptococcus pneumoniae*, which causes pneumococcal pneumonia, meningitis, septicemia, and other respiratory tract infections. Encapsulated strains of *S. pneumoniae* are more virulent than nonencapsulated strains and are more likely to invade the bloodstream and cause septicemia and meningitis.

Toxins

In addition to exoenzymes, certain pathogens are able to produce **toxins**, biological poisons that assist in their ability to invade and cause damage to tissues. Toxins can be categorized as endotoxins or exotoxins. The lipopolysaccharide (LPS) found on the outer membrane of gram-negative bacteria is called **endotoxin**. During infection and disease, gram-negative bacterial pathogens release endotoxin either when the cell dies, resulting in the disintegration of the membrane, or when the bacterium undergoes binary fission. The lipid component of endotoxin, lipid A, is responsible for the toxic properties of the LPS molecule. Lipid A is relatively conserved across different genera of gram-negative bacteria; therefore, the toxic properties of lipid A are similar regardless of the gram-negative pathogen. Lipid A triggers the immune system's inflammatory response. If the concentration of endotoxin in the body is low, the inflammatory response may provide the host an effective defense against infection; on the other hand, high concentrations of endotoxin in the blood can cause an excessive inflammatory response, leading to a severe drop in blood pressure, multi-organ failure, and death.

Exotoxins are protein molecules that are produced by a wide variety of living pathogenic bacteria. Although some gram-negative pathogens produce exotoxins, the majority are produced by gram-positive pathogens. Exotoxins differ from endotoxin in several other key characteristics, summarized in Table 2. In contrast to endotoxin, which stimulates a general systemic inflammatory response when released, exotoxins are much more specific in their action and the cells they interact with. Each exotoxin targets specific receptors on specific cells and damages those cells through unique molecular mechanisms. Endotoxin remains stable at high temperatures, and requires heating at 121 °C (250 °F) for 45 minutes to inactivate. By contrast, most exotoxins are heat labile because of their protein structure, and many are denatured (inactivated) at temperatures above 41 °C (106 °F). As discussed earlier, endotoxin can stimulate a lethal inflammatory response at very high concentrations and has a measured LD_{50} of 0.24 mg/kg. By contrast, very small concentrations of exotoxins can be lethal. For example, botulinum toxin, which causes botulism, has an LD_{50} of 0.000001 mg/kg (240,000 times more lethal than endotoxin). Table 3 provides examples of well-characterized toxins.

Comparison of Endotoxin and Exotoxins Produced by Bacteria		
Characteristic	**Endotoxin**	**Exotoxin**
Source	Gram-negative bacteria	Gram-positive (primarily) and gram-negative bacteria
Composition	Lipid A component of lipopolysaccharide	Protein
Effect on host	General systemic symptoms of inflammation and fever	Specific damage to cells dependent upon receptor-mediated targeting of cells and specific mechanisms of action
Heat stability	Heat stable	Most are heat labile, but some are heat stable
LD_{50}	High	Low

Table 2.

Some Common Bacterial Pathogens and Associated Exotoxins		
Example	**Pathogen**	**Mechanism and Disease**
Cholera toxin	*Vibrio cholerae*	Activation of adenylate cyclase in intestinal cells, causing increased levels of cyclic adenosine monophosphate (cAMP) and secretion of fluids and electrolytes out of cell, causing diarrhea
Tetanus toxin	*Clostridium tetani*	Inhibits the release of inhibitory neurotransmitters in the central nervous system, causing spastic paralysis
Botulinum toxin	*Clostridium botulinum*	Inhibits release of the neurotransmitter acetylcholine from neurons, resulting in flaccid paralysis
Diphtheria toxin	*Corynebacterium diphtheriae*	Inhibition of protein synthesis, causing cellular death
Streptolysin	*Streptococcus pyogenes*	Proteins that assemble into pores in cell membranes, disrupting their function and killing the cell
Pneumolysin	*Streptococcus pneumoniae*	
Alpha-toxin	*Staphylococcus aureus*	
Alpha-toxin	*Clostridium perfringens*	Phospholipases that degrade cell membrane phospholipids, disrupting membrane function and killing the cell
Phospholipase C	*Pseudomonas aeruginosa*	
Beta-toxin	*Staphylococcus aureus*	

Table 3.

Notice that unlike endotoxins, exotoxins can have distinctly different actions.

Cholera toxin is an exotoxin produced by the gram-negative bacterium *Vibrio cholerae* and affects the intestines. is composed of one A subunit and five B subunits. The mechanism of action of the cholera toxin is complex but in-short, it disrupts the normal physiology of the intestinal epithelial cells and causes them to secrete excessive amounts of fluid and electrolytes into the lumen of the intestinal tract, resulting in severe "rice-water stool" diarrhea characteristic of cholera.

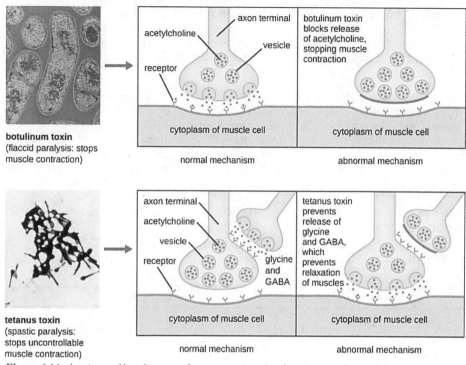

botulinum toxin
(flaccid paralysis: stops muscle contraction)

tetanus toxin
(spastic paralysis: stops uncontrollable muscle contraction)

Figure 6 Mechanisms of botulinum and tetanus toxins. (credit micrographs: modification of work by Centers for Disease Control and Prevention)

Botulinum toxin (also known as botox) is an exotoxin that acts as a neurotoxin produced by the gram-positive bacterium *Clostridium botulinum*. It is the most acutely toxic substance known to date. Normally, neurons release acetylcholine to induce muscle fiber contractions. The toxin's ability to block acetylcholine release results in the inhibition of muscle contractions, leading to muscle relaxation. This has the potential to stop breathing and cause death. Because of its action, low concentrations of botox are used for cosmetic and medical procedures, including the removal of wrinkles and treatment of overactive bladder.

Another exotoxin that acts as a neurotoxin is tetanus toxin, which is produced by the gram-positive bacterium *Clostridium tetani*. Unlike botulinum toxin, tetanus toxin binds to inhibitory interneurons, which are responsible for release of inhibitory neurotransmitters. Normally, these neurotransmitters bind to neurons at the neuromuscular junction, resulting in the inhibition of acetylcholine release. Tetanus toxin inhibits the release of neurotransmitters from the interneuron, resulting in permanent muscle contraction. The first symptom is typically stiffness of the jaw (lockjaw). Violent muscle spasms in other parts of the body follow, typically culminating with respiratory failure and death.

A final mechanism that pathogens can use to protect themselves against the immune system is called **antigenic variation**, which is the alteration of surface proteins so that a pathogen is no longer recognized by the host's immune system. For example, the bacterium *Borrelia burgdorferi*, the causative agent of Lyme disease, contains a surface lipoprotein known as VlsE. Because of genetic recombination during DNA replication and repair, this bacterial protein undergoes antigenic variation. Each time fever occurs, the VlsE protein in *B. burgdorferi* can differ so much that antibodies against previous VlsE sequences are not effective. It is believed that this variation in the VlsE contributes to the ability *B. burgdorferi* to cause chronic disease. Another important human bacterial pathogen that uses antigenic variation to avoid the immune system is *Neisseria gonorrhoeae*, which causes the sexually transmitted disease gonorrhea. This bacterium is well known for its ability to undergo antigenic variation of its type IV pili to avoid immune defenses.

Reservoir of Infection

For pathogens to persist over long periods of time they require **reservoir**s where they normally reside. Reservoirs can be living organisms or nonliving sites. Nonliving reservoirs can include soil and water in the environment. These may naturally harbor the organism because it may grow in that environment. These environments may also become contaminated with pathogens in human feces, pathogens shed by intermediate hosts, or pathogens contained in the remains of intermediate hosts.

Pathogens may have mechanisms of dormancy or resilience that allow them to survive (but typically not to reproduce) for varying periods of time in nonliving environments. For example, *Clostridium tetani* survives in the soil and in the presence of oxygen as a resistant endospore. Although many viruses are soon destroyed once in contact with air, water, or other non-physiological conditions, certain types are capable of persisting outside of a living cell for varying amounts of time. For example, a study that looked at the ability of influenza viruses to infect a cell culture after varying amounts of time on a banknote showed survival times from 48 hours to 17 days, depending on how they were deposited on the banknote. On the other hand, cold-causing rhinoviruses are somewhat fragile, typically surviving less than a day outside of physiological fluids.

A human acting as a reservoir of a pathogen may or may not be capable of transmitting the pathogen, depending on the stage of infection and the pathogen. To help prevent the spread of disease among school children, the CDC has developed guidelines based on the risk of transmission during the course of the disease. For example, children with chickenpox are considered contagious for five days from the start of the rash, whereas children with most gastrointestinal illnesses should be kept home for 24 hours after the symptoms disappear.

An individual capable of transmitting a pathogen without displaying symptoms is referred to as a carrier. A **passive carrier** is contaminated with the pathogen and can mechanically transmit it to another host; however, a passive carrier is not infected. For example, a health-care professional who fails to wash his hands after seeing a patient harboring an infectious agent could become a passive carrier, transmitting the pathogen to another patient who becomes infected.

By contrast, an **active carrier** is an infected individual who can transmit the disease to others. An active carrier may or may not exhibit signs or symptoms of infection. For example, active carriers may transmit the disease during the incubation period (before they show signs and symptoms) or the period of convalescence (after symptoms have subsided). Active carriers who do not present signs or symptoms of disease despite infection are called **asymptomatic carrier**s. Pathogens such as hepatitis B virus, herpes simplex virus, and HIV are frequently transmitted by asymptomatic carriers. Mary Mallon, better known as Typhoid Mary, is a famous historical example of an asymptomatic carrier. An Irish immigrant, Mallon worked as a cook for households in and around New York City between 1900 and 1915. In each household, the residents developed typhoid fever (caused by *Salmonella typhi*) a few weeks after Mallon started working. Later investigations determined that Mallon was responsible for at least 122 cases of typhoid fever, five of which were fatal.

A pathogen may have more than one living reservoir. In zoonotic diseases or **zoonoses**, animals act as reservoirs of human disease and transmit the infectious agent to humans through direct or indirect contact. In some cases, the disease also affects the animal, but in other cases the animal is asymptomatic.

Typhoid Fever

Certain serotypes of *Salmonella. enterica*, primarily serotype Typhi (*S. typhi*) but also Paratyphi, cause a more severe type of salmonellosis called **typhoid fever**. This serious illness, which has an untreated mortality rate of 10%, causes high fever, body aches, headache, nausea, lethargy, and a possible rash.

Some individuals carry *S. typhi* without presenting signs or symptoms (known as asymptomatic carriers) and continually shed them through their feces. These carriers often have the bacteria in the gallbladder or intestinal epithelium. Individuals consuming food or water contaminated with these feces can become infected.

S. typhi penetrate the intestinal mucosa, grow within the macrophages, and are transported through the body, most notably to the liver and gallbladder. Eventually, the macrophages lyse, releasing *S. typhi* into the bloodstream and lymphatic system. Mortality can result from ulceration and perforation of the intestine. A wide range of complications, such as pneumonia and jaundice, can occur with disseminated disease.

Typhoid Mary

Mary Mallon was an Irish immigrant who worked as a cook in New York in the early 20th century. Over seven years, from 1900 to 1907, Mallon worked for a number of different households, unknowingly spreading illness to the people who lived in each one. In 1906, one family hired George Soper, an expert in typhoid fever epidemics, to determine the cause of the illnesses in their household. Eventually, Soper tracked Mallon down and directly linked 22 cases of typhoid fever to her. He discovered that Mallon was a carrier for typhoid but was immune to it herself. Although active carriers had been recognized before, this was the first time that an asymptomatic carrier of infection had been identified.

Because she herself had never been ill, Mallon found it difficult to believe she could be the source of the illness. She fled from Soper and the authorities because she did not want to be quarantined or forced to give up her profession, which was relatively well paid for someone with her background. However, Mallon was eventually caught and kept in an isolation facility in the Bronx, where she remained until 1910, when the New York health department released her under the condition that she never again work with food. Unfortunately, Mallon did not comply, and she soon began working as a cook again. After new cases began to appear that resulted in the death of two individuals, the authorities tracked her down again and returned her to isolation, where she remained for 23 more years until her death in 1938. Epidemiologists were able to trace 51 cases of typhoid fever and three deaths directly to Mallon, who is unflatteringly remembered as "Typhoid Mary."

The Typhoid Mary case has direct correlations in the health-care industry. Consider Kaci Hickox, an American nurse who treated Ebola patients in West Africa during the 2014 epidemic. After returning to the United States, Hickox was quarantined against her will for three days and later found not to have Ebola. Hickox vehemently opposed the quarantine. In an editorial published in the British newspaper *The Guardian*, Hickox argued that quarantining asymptomatic health-care workers who had not tested positive for a disease would not only prevent such individuals from practicing their profession, but discourage others from volunteering to work in disease-ridden areas where health-care workers are desperately needed.

Modes of Disease Transmission

Understanding how infectious pathogens spread is critical to preventing infectious disease. Many pathogens require a living host to survive, while others may be able to persist in a dormant state outside of a living host. But having infected one host, all pathogens must also have a mechanism of transfer from one host to another or they will die when their host dies. Pathogens often have elaborate adaptations to exploit host biology, behavior, and ecology to live in and move between hosts. Hosts have evolved defenses against pathogens, but because their rates of evolution are typically slower than their pathogens (because their generation times are longer), hosts are

Figure 7 *Direct contact transmission of pathogens can occur through physical contact. Many pathogens require contact with a mucous membrane to enter the body, but the host may transfer the pathogen from another point of contact (e.g., hand) to a mucous membrane (e.g., mouth or eye). (credit left: modification of work by Lisa Doehnert)*

usually at an evolutionary disadvantage. This section will explore where pathogens survive—both inside and outside hosts—and some of the many ways they move from one host to another.

Regardless of the reservoir, transmission must occur for an infection to spread. First, transmission from the reservoir to the individual must occur. Then, the individual must transmit the infectious agent to other susceptible individuals, either directly or indirectly. Pathogenic microorganisms employ diverse transmission mechanisms.

Figure 8 *Aerosols produced by sneezing, coughing, or even just speaking are an important mechanism for respiratory pathogen transmission. Simple actions, like covering your mouth when coughing or sneezing, can reduce the spread of these microbes. (credit: modification of work by Centers for Disease Control and Prevention)*

Contact transmission includes direct contact or indirect contact. Person-to-person transmission is a form **of direct contact transmission**. Here the agent is transmitted by physical contact between two individuals through actions such as touching, kissing, sexual intercourse, or droplet sprays. Often, contact between mucous membranes is required for entry of the pathogen into the new host, although skin-to-skin contact can lead to mucous membrane contact if the new host subsequently touches a mucous membrane. Contact transmission may also be site-specific; for example, some diseases can be transmitted by sexual contact but not by other forms of contact.

When an individual coughs or sneezes, small droplets of mucus that may contain pathogens are ejected. This leads to direct droplet transmission, which refers to **droplet transmission** of a pathogen to a new host over distances of one meter or less. A wide variety of diseases are transmitted by droplets, including influenza and many forms of pneumonia. Transmission over distances greater than one meter is called **airborne transmission**.

Indirect contact transmission involves inanimate objects called **fomites** that become contaminated by pathogens from an infected individual or reservoir. For example, an individual with the common cold may sneeze, causing droplets to land on a fomite such as a tablecloth or carpet, or the individual may wipe her nose and then transfer mucus to a fomite such as a doorknob or towel. Transmission occurs indirectly when a new susceptible host later touches the fomite and transfers the contaminated material to a susceptible portal of entry. Fomites can also include objects used in clinical settings that are not

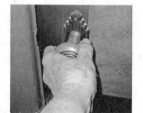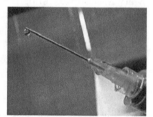

Figure 9 *Fomites are nonliving objects that facilitate the indirect transmission of pathogens. Contaminated doorknobs, towels, and syringes are all common examples of fomites. (credit left: modification of work by Kate Ter Haar; credit middle: modification of work by Vernon Swanepoel; credit right: modification of work by "Zaldylmg"/Flickr)*

properly sterilized, such as syringes, needles, catheters, and surgical equipment. Pathogens transmitted indirectly via such fomites are a major cause of healthcare-associated infections.

Figure 10 *Food is an important vehicle of transmission for pathogens, especially of the gastrointestinal and upper respiratory systems. Notice the glass shield above the food trays, designed to prevent pathogens ejected in coughs and sneezes from entering the food. (credit: Fort George G. Meade Public Affairs Office)*

The term **vehicle transmission** refers to the transmission of pathogens through vehicles such as water, food, air, and body fluids. Water contamination through poor sanitation methods leads to waterborne transmission of disease. Waterborne disease remains a serious problem in many regions throughout the world. The World Health Organization (WHO) estimates that contaminated drinking water is responsible for more than 500,000 deaths each year. Similarly, food contaminated through poor handling or storage can lead to foodborne transmission of disease.

Dust and fine particles known as aerosols, which can float in the air, can carry pathogens and facilitate the airborne transmission of disease. For example, dust particles are the dominant mode of transmission of hantavirus to humans. Hantavirus is found in mouse feces, urine, and saliva, but when these substances dry, they can disintegrate into fine particles that can become airborne when disturbed; inhalation of these particles can lead to a serious and sometimes fatal respiratory infection.

Although droplet transmission over short distances is considered contact transmission as discussed above, longer distance transmission of droplets through the air is considered vehicle transmission. Unlike larger particles that drop quickly out of the air column, fine mucus droplets produced by coughs or sneezes can remain suspended for long periods of time, traveling considerable distances. In certain conditions, droplets desiccate quickly to produce a droplet nucleus that is capable of transmitting pathogens; air temperature and humidity can have an impact on effectiveness of airborne transmission.

Tuberculosis is often transmitted via airborne transmission when the causative agent, *Mycobacterium tuberculosis*, is released in small particles with coughs. Because tuberculosis requires as few as 10 microbes to initiate a new infection, patients with tuberculosis must be treated in rooms equipped with special ventilation, and anyone entering the room should wear a mask.

Diseases can also be transmitted by a mechanical or biological vector, an animal (typically an arthropod) that carries the disease from one host to another. Mechanical transmission is facilitated by a mechanical vector, an animal that carries a pathogen from one host to another without being infected itself. For example, a fly may land on fecal matter and later transmit bacteria from the feces to food that it lands on; a

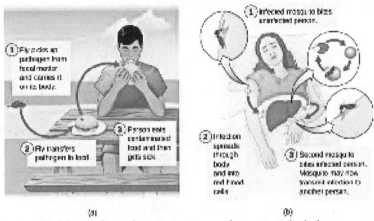

Figure 11 (a) A mechanical vector carries a pathogen on its body from one host to another, not as an infection. (b) A biological vector carries a pathogen from one host to another after becoming infected itself.

human eating the food may then become infected by the bacteria, resulting in a case of diarrhea or dyseBiological transmission occurs when the pathogen reproduces within a biological vector that transmits the pathogen from one host to another. Arthropods are the main vectors responsible for biological transmission. Most arthropod vectors transmit the pathogen by biting the host, creating a wound that serves as a portal of entry. The pathogen may go through part of its reproductive cycle in the gut or salivary glands of the arthropod to facilitate its transmission through the bite. For example, hemipterans (called "kissing bugs" or "assassin bugs") transmit Chagas disease to humans by defecating when they bite, after which the human scratches or rubs the infected feces into a mucous membrane or break in the skin.

Biological insect vectors include mosquitoes, which transmit malaria and other diseases, and lice, which transmit typhus. Other arthropod vectors can include arachnids, primarily ticks, which transmit Lyme disease and other diseases, and mites, which transmit scrub typhus and rickettsial pox. Biological transmission, because it involves survival and reproduction within a parasitized vector, complicates the biology of the pathogen and its transmission. There are also important non-arthropod vectors of disease, including mammals and birds. Various species of mammals can transmit rabies to humans, usually by means of a bite that transmits the rabies virus. Chickens and other domestic poultry can transmit avian influenza to humans through direct or indirect contact with avian influenza virus A shed in the birds' saliva, mucous, and feces.

Common Arthropod Vectors and Select Pathogens			
Vector	Species	Pathogen	Disease
Black fly	Simulium spp.	Onchocerca volvulus	Onchocerciasis (river blindness)
Flea	Xenopsylla cheopis	Rickettsia typhi	Murine typhus
		Yersinia pestis	Plague
Kissing bug	Triatoma spp.	Trypanosoma cruzi	Chagas disease
Louse	Pediculus humanus humanus	Bartonella quintana	Trench fever
		Borrelia recurrentis	Relapsing fever
		Rickettsia prowazekii	Typhus
Mite (chigger)	Leptotrombidium spp.	Orientia tsutsugamushi	Scrub typhus
	Liponyssoides sanguineus	Rickettsia akari	Rickettsialpox
Mosquito	Aedes spp. Haemagogus spp.	Yellow fever virus	Yellow fever
	Anopheles spp.	Plasmodium falciparum	Malaria
	Culex pipiens	West Nile virus	West Nile disease
Sand fly	Phlebotomus spp.	Leishmania spp.	Leishmaniasis
Tick	Ixodes spp.	Borrelia spp.	Lyme disease
	Dermacentor spp. and others	Rickettsia rickettsii	Rocky Mountain spotted fever
Tsetse fly	Glossina spp.	Trypanosoma brucei	African trypanosomiasis (sleeping sickness)

Figure 12 (credit "Black fly", "Tick", "Tsetse fly": modification of work by USDA; credit: "Flea": modification of work by Centers for Disease Control and Prevention; credit: "Louse", "Mosquito", "Sand fly": modification of work by James Gathany, Centers for Disease Control and Prevention; credit "Kissing bug": modification of work by Glenn Seplak; credit "Mite": modification of work by Michael Wunderli)

Portal of Entry

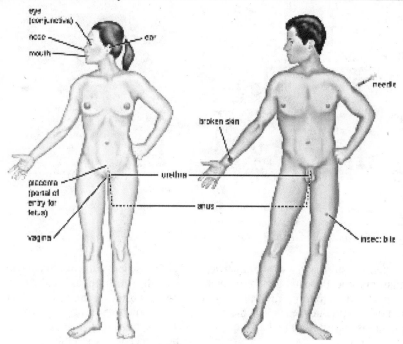

Figure 13. Shown are different portals of entry where pathogens can gain access into the body. With the exception of the placenta, many of these locations are directly exposed to the external environment.

An encounter with a potential pathogen is known as exposure or contact. The food we eat and the objects we handle are all ways that we can come into contact with potential pathogens. Yet, not all contacts result in infection and disease. For a pathogen to cause disease, it needs to be able to gain access into host tissue. An anatomic site through which pathogens can pass into host tissue is called a **portal of entry**. These are locations where the host cells are in direct contact with the external environment. Major portals of entry include the **skin, mucous membranes, placenta,** and **parenteral routes.**

Mucosal surfaces are the most important portals of entry for microbes; these include the mucous membranes of the respiratory tract, the gastrointestinal tract, and the genitourinary tract. Although most mucosal surfaces are in the interior of the body, some are contiguous with the external skin at various body openings, including the eyes, nose, mouth, urethra, and anus.

The respiratory tract is one of the main portals of entry into the human body for microbial pathogens. On average, a human takes about 20,000 breaths each day. This roughly corresponds to 10,000 liters, or 10 cubic meters, of air. Suspended within this volume of air are millions of microbes of terrestrial, animal, and human origin—including many potential pathogens. A few of these pathogens will cause relatively mild infections like sore throats and colds. Others, however, are less benign. According to the World Health Organization, respiratory tract infections such as tuberculosis, influenza, and pneumonia were responsible for more than 4 million deaths worldwide in 2012.

Most pathogens are suited to a particular portal of entry. A pathogen's portal specificity is determined by the organism's environmental adaptions and by the enzymes and toxins they secrete. The respiratory and gastrointestinal tracts are particularly vulnerable portals of entry because particles that include microorganisms are constantly inhaled or ingested, respectively.

Pathogens can also enter through a breach in the protective barriers of the skin and mucous membranes. Pathogens that enter the body in this way are said to enter by the **parenteral** route. For example, the skin is a good natural barrier to pathogens, but breaks in the skin (e.g., wounds, insect bites, animal bites, needle pricks) can provide a parenteral portal of entry for microorganisms.

In pregnant women, the placenta normally prevents microorganisms from passing from the mother to the fetus. However, a few pathogens are capable of crossing the blood-placental barrier. The gram-positive bacterium Listeria monocytogenes, which causes the foodborne disease listeriosis, is one example that poses a serious risk to the fetus and can sometimes lead to spontaneous abortion. Other pathogens that can pass the placental barrier to infect the fetus are known collectively by the acronym TORCH.

Transmission of infectious diseases from mother to baby is also a concern at the time of birth when the baby passes through the birth canal. Babies whose mothers have active chlamydia or gonorrhea infections may be exposed to the causative pathogens in the vagina, which can result in eye infections that lead to blindness. To prevent this, it is standard practice to administer antibiotic drops to infants' eyes shortly after birth.

Pathogens Capable of Crossing the Placental Barrier (TORCH Infections)

	Disease	Pathogen
T	Toxoplasmosis	*Taxoplasma gondii* (protozoan)
O	Syphilis Chickenpox Hepatitis B HIV Fifth disease (erythema infectiosum)	*Treponema pallidum* (bacterium) Varicella-zoster virus (human herpesvirus 3) Hepatitis B virus (hepadnavirus) Retrovirus Parvovirus B19
R	Rubella (German measles)	Togavirus
C	Cytomegalovirus	Human herpesvirus 5
H	Herpes	Herpes simplex viruses (HSV) 1 and 2

Table 4

Following invasion, successful multiplication of the pathogen leads to infection. Infections can be described as local, focal, or systemic, depending on the extent of the infection. A **local infection** is confined to a small area of the body, typically near the portal of entry. For example, a hair follicle infected by *Staphylococcus aureus* infection may result in a boil around the site of infection, but the bacterium is largely contained to this small location. Other examples of local infections that involve more extensive tissue involvement include urinary tract infections confined to the bladder or pneumonia confined to the lungs.

In a **focal infection**, a localized pathogen, or the toxins it produces, can spread to a secondary location. For example, a dental hygienist nicking the gum with a sharp tool can lead to a local infection in the gum by *Streptococcus* bacteria of the normal oral microbiota. These *Streptococcus* spp. may then gain access to the bloodstream and make their way to other locations in the body, resulting in a secondary infection.

When an infection becomes disseminated throughout the body, we call it a **systemic infection**. For example, infection by the varicella-zoster virus typically gains entry through a mucous membrane of the upper respiratory system. It then spreads throughout the body, resulting in the classic red skin lesions associated with chickenpox. Since these lesions are not sites of initial infection, they are signs of a systemic infection.

Sometimes a **primary infection**, the initial infection caused by one pathogen, can lead to a **secondary infection** by another pathogen. For example, the immune system of a patient with a primary infection by HIV becomes compromised, making the patient more susceptible to secondary diseases like oral thrush and others caused by opportunistic pathogens. Similarly, a primary infection by Influenzavirus damages and decreases the defense mechanisms of the lungs, making patients more susceptible to a secondary pneumonia by a bacterial pathogen like *Haemophilus influenzae* or *Streptococcus pneumoniae*. Some secondary infections can even develop as a result of treatment for a primary infection. Antibiotic therapy targeting the primary pathogen can cause collateral damage to the normal microbiota, creating an opening for opportunistic pathogen.

Portal of Exit

For a pathogen to persist, it must put itself in a position to be transmitted to a new host, leaving the infected host through a **portal of exit**. As with portals of entry, many pathogens are adapted to use a particular portal of exit. Similar to portals of entry, the most common portals of exit include the skin and the respiratory, urogenital, and gastrointestinal tracts. Coughing and sneezing can expel pathogens from the respiratory tract. A single sneeze can send thousands of virus particles into the air. Secretions and excretions can transport pathogens out of other portals of exit. Feces, urine, semen, vaginal secretions, tears, sweat, and shed skin cells can all serve as vehicles for a pathogen to leave the body. Pathogens that rely on insect vectors for transmission exit the body in the blood extracted by a biting insect. Similarly, some pathogens exit the body in blood extracted by needles.

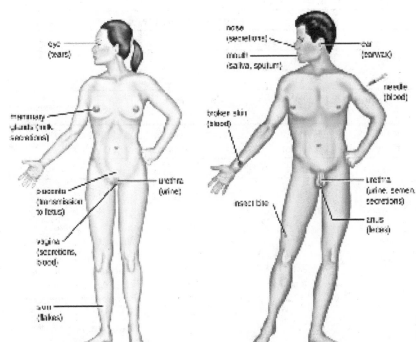

Figure 14 Pathogens leave the body of an infected host through various portals of exit to infect new hosts.

Classifications of Disease

The World Health Organization's (WHO) International Classification of Diseases (ICD) is used in clinical fields to classify diseases and monitor **morbidity** (the number of cases of a disease) and **mortality** (the number of deaths due to a disease). In this section, we will introduce terminology used by the ICD (and in health-care professions in general) to describe and categorize various types of disease.

An **infectious disease** is any disease caused by the direct effect of a pathogen. A pathogen may be cellular (bacteria, parasites, and fungi) or acellular (viruses and prions). Some infectious diseases are also **communicable**, meaning they are capable of being spread from person to person through either direct or indirect mechanisms. Some infectious communicable diseases are also considered **contagious** diseases, meaning they are easily spread from person to person. Not all contagious diseases are equally so; the degree to which a disease is contagious usually depends on how the pathogen is transmitted. For example, measles is a highly contagious viral disease that can be transmitted when an infected person coughs or sneezes and an uninfected person breathes in droplets containing the virus. Gonorrhea is not as contagious as measles because transmission of the pathogen (*Neisseria gonorrhoeae*) requires close intimate contact (usually sexual) between an infected person and an uninfected person.

Diseases acquired in hospital settings are known as **nosocomial disease**s. Several factors contribute to the prevalence and severity of nosocomial diseases. First, sick patients bring numerous pathogens into hospitals, and some of these pathogens can be transmitted easily via improperly sterilized medical equipment, bed sheets, call buttons, door handles, or by clinicians, nurses, or therapists who do not wash their hands before touching a patient. Second, many hospital patients have weakened immune systems, making them more susceptible to infections. Compounding this, the prevalence of antibiotics in hospital settings can select for drug-resistant bacteria that can cause very serious infections that are difficult to treat.

Certain infectious diseases are not transmitted between humans directly but can be transmitted from animals to humans. Such a disease is called **zoonotic disease (or zoonosis).** According to WHO, a zoonosis is a disease that occurs when a pathogen is transferred from a vertebrate animal to a human; however, sometimes the term is defined more broadly to include diseases transmitted by all animals (including invertebrates). For example, rabies is a viral zoonotic disease spread from animals to humans through bites and contact with infected saliva. Many other zoonotic diseases rely on insects or other arthropods for transmission. Examples include yellow fever (transmitted through the bite of mosquitoes infected with yellow fever virus) and Rocky Mountain spotted fever (transmitted through the bite of ticks infected with *Rickettsia rickettsii*).

In contrast to communicable infectious diseases, a **noncommunicable** infectious disease is not spread from one person to another. One example is tetanus, caused by *Clostridium tetani*, a bacterium that produces endospores that can survive in the soil for many years. This disease is typically only transmitted through contact with a skin wound; it cannot be passed from an infected person to another person. Similarly, Legionnaires disease is caused by *Legionella pneumophila*, a bacterium that lives within amoebae in moist locations like water-cooling towers. An individual may contract Legionnaires disease via contact with the contaminated water, but once infected, the individual cannot pass the pathogen to other individuals.

In addition to the wide variety of noncommunicable infectious diseases, **noninfectious disease**s (those not caused by pathogens) are an important cause of morbidity and mortality worldwide. Noninfectious diseases can be caused by a wide variety factors, including genetics, the environment, or immune system dysfunction, to name a few. For example, sickle cell anemia is an inherited disease caused by a genetic mutation that can be passed from parent to offspring.

Types of Noninfectious Diseases		
Type	Definition	Example
Inherited	A genetic disease	Sickle cell anemia
Congenital	Disease that is present at or before birth	Down syndrome
Degenerative	Progressive, irreversible loss of function	Parkinson disease (affecting central nervous system)
Nutritional deficiency	Impaired body function due to lack of nutrients	Scurvy (vitamin C deficiency)
Endocrine	Disease involving malfunction of glands that release hormones to regulate body functions	Hypothyroidism – thyroid does not produce enough thyroid hormone, which is important for metabolism
Neoplastic	Abnormal growth (benign or malignant)	Some forms of cancer

Table 5

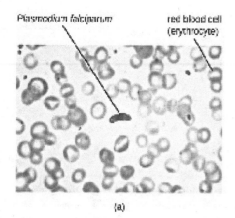
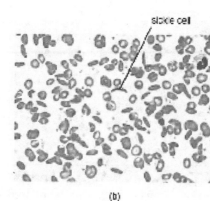

Figure 15 Blood smears showing two diseases of the blood. (a) Malaria is an infectious, zoonotic disease caused by the protozoan pathogen Plasmodium falciparum (shown here) and several other species of the genus Plasmodium. It is transmitted by mosquitoes to humans. (b) Sickle cell disease is a noninfectious genetic disorder that results in abnormally shaped red blood cells, which can stick together and obstruct the flow of blood through the circulatory system. It is not caused by a pathogen, but rather a genetic mutation. (credit a: modification of work by Centers for Disease Control and Prevention; credit b: modification of work by Ed Uthman)

Acute and Chronic Diseases

The duration of the period of illness can vary greatly, depending on the pathogen, effectiveness of the immune response in the host, and any medical treatment received. For an **acute disease**, pathologic changes occur over a relatively short time (e.g., hours, days, or a few weeks) and involve a rapid onset of disease conditions. For example, influenza (caused by Influenzavirus) is considered an acute disease because the incubation period is approximately 1–2 days. Infected individuals can spread influenza to others for approximately 5 days after becoming ill. After approximately 1 week, individuals enter the period of decline.

For a **chronic disease**, pathologic changes can occur over longer time spans (e.g., months, years, or a lifetime). For example, chronic gastritis (inflammation of the lining of the stomach) is caused by the gram-negative bacterium *Helicobacter pylori*. *H. pylori* is able to colonize the stomach and persist in its highly acidic environment by producing the enzyme urease, which modifies the local acidity, allowing the bacteria to survive indefinitely. Consequently, *H. pylori* infections can recur indefinitely unless the infection is cleared using antibiotics. Hepatitis B virus can cause a chronic infection in some patients who do not eliminate the virus after the acute illness. A chronic infection with hepatitis B virus is characterized by the continued production of infectious virus for 6 months or longer after the acute infection, as measured by the presence of viral antigen in blood samples.

In **latent disease**s, as opposed to chronic infectious disease, the causal pathogen goes dormant for extended periods of time with no active replication. Examples of diseases that go into a latent state after the acute infection include herpes (herpes simplex viruses [HSV-1 and HSV-2]), chickenpox (varicella-zoster virus [VZV]), and mononucleosis (Epstein-Barr virus [EBV]). HSV-1, HSV-2, and VZV evade the host immune system by residing in a latent form within cells of the nervous system for long periods of time, but they can reactivate to become active infections during times of stress and immunosuppression. For example, an initial infection by VZV may result in a case of childhood chickenpox, followed by a long period of latency. The virus may reactivate decades later, causing episodes of shingles in adulthood. EBV goes into latency in B cells of the immune system and possibly epithelial cells; it can reactivate years later to produce B-cell lymphoma.

Disease and Epidemiology

The field of **epidemiology** concerns the geographical distribution and timing of infectious disease occurrences and how they are transmitted and maintained in nature, with the goal of recognizing and controlling outbreaks. The science of epidemiology includes **etiology** (the study of the causes of disease) and investigation of disease transmission (mechanisms by which a disease is spread).

Patterns of Incidence

Diseases that are seen only occasionally, and usually without geographic concentration, are called **sporadic diseases.** Examples of sporadic diseases include tetanus, rabies, and plague. In the United States, *Clostridium tetani*, the bacterium that causes tetanus, is ubiquitous in the soil environment, but incidences of infection occur only rarely and in scattered locations because most individuals are vaccinated, clean wounds appropriately, or are only rarely in a situation that would cause infection.[3] Likewise in the United States there are a few scattered cases of plague each year, usually contracted from rodents in rural areas in the western states.[4]

Diseases that are constantly present (often at a low level) in a population within a particular geographic region are called **endemic disease**s. For example, malaria is endemic to some regions of Brazil, but is not endemic to the United States.

Diseases for which a larger than expected number of cases occurs in a short time within a geographic region are called **epidemic disease**s. Influenza is a good example of a commonly epidemic disease. Incidence patterns of influenza tend to rise each winter in the northern hemisphere. These seasonal increases are expected, so it would not be accurate to say that influenza is epidemic every winter; however, some winters have an usually large number of seasonal influenza cases in particular regions, and such situations would qualify as epidemics.

An epidemic disease signals the breakdown of an equilibrium in disease frequency, often resulting from some change in environmental conditions or in the population. In the case of influenza, the disruption can be due to antigenic shift or drift which allows influenza virus strains to circumvent the acquired immunity of their human hosts.

An epidemic that occurs on a worldwide scale is called a **pandemic disease**. For example, HIV/AIDS is a pandemic disease and novel influenza virus strains often become pandemic.

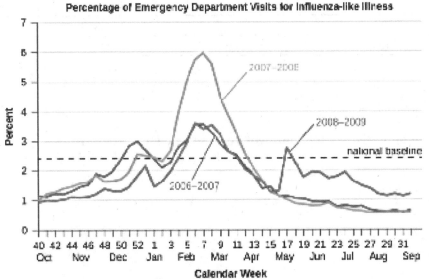

Figure 16 The 2007–2008 influenza season in the United States saw much higher than normal numbers of visits to emergency departments for influenza-like symptoms as compared to the previous and the following years. (credit: modification of work by Centers for Disease Control and Prevention)

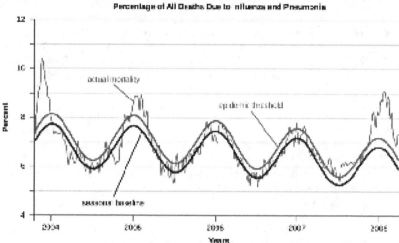

Figure 17 The seasonal epidemic threshold (blue curve) is set by the CDC-based data from the previous five years. When actual mortality rates exceed this threshold, a disease is considered to be epidemic. As this graph shows, pneumonia- and influenza-related mortality saw pronounced epidemics during the winters of 2003–2004, 2005, and 2008. (credit: modification of work by Centers for Disease Control and Prevention)

Etiology

When studying an epidemic, an epidemiologist's first task is to determinate the cause of the disease, called the **etiologic agent** or **causative agent**. Connecting a disease to a specific pathogen can be challenging because of the extra effort typically required to demonstrate direct causation as opposed to a simple association. It is not enough to observe an association between a disease and a suspected pathogen; controlled experiments are needed to eliminate other possible causes. In addition, pathogens are typically difficult to detect when there is no immediate clue as to what is causing the outbreak. Signs and symptoms of disease are also commonly nonspecific, meaning that many different agents can give rise to the same set of signs and symptoms. This complicates diagnosis even when a causative agent is familiar to scientists.

The Role of Public Health Organizations

The main national public health agency in the United States is the **Centers for Disease Control and Prevention (CDC)**, an agency of the Department of Health and Human Services. The CDC is charged with protecting the public from disease and injury. One way that the CDC carries out this mission is by overseeing the National Notifiable Disease Surveillance System (NNDSS) in cooperation with regional, state, and territorial public health departments. The NNDSS monitors diseases considered to be of public health importance on a national scale. Such diseases are called **notifiable disease**s or **reportable disease**s because all cases must be reported to the CDC. A physician treating a patient with a notifiable disease is legally required to submit a report on the case. Notifiable diseases include HIV infection, measles, West Nile virus infections, and many others. Some states have their own lists of notifiable diseases that include diseases beyond those on the CDC's list.

Notifiable diseases are tracked by epidemiological studies and the data is used to inform health-care providers and the public about possible risks. The CDC publishes the ***Morbidity and Mortality Weekly Report* (*MMWR*),** which provides physicians and health-care workers with updates on public health issues and the latest data pertaining to notifiable diseases. The following table is an example of the kind of data contained in the *MMWR*.

Incidence of Four Notifiable Diseases in the United States, Week Ending January 2, 2016				
Disease	Current Week (Jan 2, 2016)	Median of Previous 52 Weeks	Maximum of Previous 52 Weeks	Cumulative Cases 2015
Campylobacteriosis	406	869	1,385	46,618
***Chlamydia trachomatis* infection**	11,024	28,562	31,089	1,425,303
Giardiasis	115	230	335	11,870
Gonorrhea	3,207	7,155	8,283	369,926

Table 6

The current *Morbidity and Mortality Weekly Report* is available online.

2019 Nationally Notifiable diseases (clicking on a disease will connect you to the CDC website)

- Anthrax
- Arboviral diseases, neuroinvasive and non-neuroinvasive
- California serogroup virus diseases
- Chikungunya virus disease
- Eastern equine encephalitis virus disease
- Powassan virus disease
- St. Louis encephalitis virus disease
- West Nile virus disease

- Western equine encephalitis virus disease
- Babesiosis
- Botulism
- Botulism, foodborne
- Botulism, infant
- Botulism, wound
- Botulism, other
- Brucellosis
- Campylobacteriosis
- Cancer
- *Candida auris*, clinical
- Carbapenemase Producing Carbapenem
- Resistant Enterobacteriaceae (CP-CRE)
- CP-CRE, *Enterobacter* spp.
- CP-CRE, *Escherichia coli* (*E. coli*)
- CP-CRE, *Klebsiella* spp.
- Carbon monoxide poisoning
- Chancroid
- *Chlamydia trachomatis* infection
- Cholera
- Coccidioidomycosis
- Congenital syphilis
- Syphilitic stillbirth
- Cryptosporidiosis
- Cyclosporiasis
- Dengue virus infections
- Dengue
- Dengue-like illness
- Severe dengue
- Diphtheria
- Ehrlichiosis and anaplasmosis
- *Anaplasma phagocytophilum* infection
- *Ehrlichia chaffeensis* infection
- *Ehrlichia ewingii* infection
- Undetermined human ehrlichiosis/anaplasmosis
- Foodborne Disease Outbreak
- Giardiasis
- Gonorrhea

- *Haemophilus influenzae*, invasive disease
- Hansen's disease
- Hantavirus infection, non-Hantavirus pulmonary syndrome
- Hantavirus pulmonary syndrome
- Hemolytic uremic syndrome, post-diarrheal
- Hepatitis A, acute
- Hepatitis B, acute
- Hepatitis B, chronic
- Hepatitis B, perinatal virus infection
- Hepatitis C, acute
- Hepatitis C, chronic
- Hepatitis C, perinatal infection
- HIV infection (AIDS has been reclassified as HIV Stage III)
- Influenza-associated pediatric mortality
- Invasive pneumococcal disease
- Lead, elevated blood levels
- Lead, elevated blood levels, children (<16 Years)
- Lead, elevated blood levels, adult (≥16 Years)
- Legionellosis
- Leptospirosis
- Listeriosis
- Lyme disease
- Malaria
- Measles
- Meningococcal disease
- Mumps
- Novel influenza A virus infections
- Pertussis
- Pesticide-related illness and injury, acute
- Plague
- Poliomyelitis, paralytic
- Poliovirus infection, nonparalytic
- Psittacosis
- Q fever
- Q fever, acute
- Q fever, chronic
- Rabies, animal
- Rabies, human

- Rubella

- Rubella, congenital syndrome

- *Salmonella* Paratyphi infection (*Salmonella enterica* serotypes Paratyphi A, B [tartrate negative], and C [*S.* Paratyphi])

- *Salmonella* Typhi infection (*Salmonella enterica* serotype Typhi)

- Salmonellosis

- Severe acute respiratory syndrome-associated coronavirus disease

- Shiga toxin-producing *Escherichia coli*

- Shigellosis

- Silicosis

- Smallpox

- Spotted fever rickettsiosis

- Streptococcal toxic shock syndrome

- Syphilis

- Syphilis, primary

- Syphilis, secondary

- Syphilis, early non-primary non-secondary

- Syphilis, unknown duration or late

- Tetanus

- Toxic shock syndrome (other than streptococcal)

- Trichinellosis

- Tuberculosis

- Tularemia

- Vancomycin-intermediate *Staphylococcus aureus* and Vancomycin-resistant *Staphylococcus aureus*

- Varicella

- Varicella deaths

- Vibriosis

- Viral hemorrhagic fever

- Crimean-Congo hemorrhagic fever virus

- Ebola virus

- Lassa virus

- Lujo virus

- Marburg virus

- New World arenavirus – Guanarito virus

- New World arenavirus – Junin virus

- New World arenavirus – Machupo virus

- New World arenavirus – Sabia virus

- Waterborne Disease Outbreak

- Yellow Fever

- [Zika virus disease and Zika virus infection](#)
- [Zika virus disease, congenital](#)
- [Zika virus disease, non-congenital](#)
- [Zika virus infection, congenital](#)
- [Zika virus infection, non-congenital](#)

In 2011, more than 720,000 HAIs occurred in hospitals in the United States, according to the CDC. About 22% of these HAIs occurred at a surgical site, and cases of pneumonia accounted for another 22%; urinary tract infections accounted for an additional 13%, and primary bloodstream infections 10%. Such HAIs often occur when pathogens are introduced to patients' bodies through contaminated surgical or medical equipment, such as catheters and respiratory ventilators. Health-care facilities seek to limit nosocomial infections through training and hygiene protocols.

Global Public Health

A large number of international programs and agencies are involved in efforts to promote global public health. Among their goals are developing infrastructure in health care, public sanitation, and public health capacity; monitoring infectious disease occurrences around the world; coordinating communications between national public health agencies in various countries; and coordinating international responses to major health crises. In large part, these international efforts are necessary because disease-causing microorganisms know no national boundaries.

The World Health Organization (WHO)

International public health issues are coordinated by the **World Health Organization (WHO),** an agency of the United Nations. Of its roughly $4 billion budget for 2015–16, about $1 billion was funded by member states and the remaining $3 billion by voluntary contributions. In addition to monitoring and reporting on infectious disease, WHO also develops and implements strategies for their control and prevention. WHO has had a number of successful international public health campaigns. For example, its vaccination program against smallpox, begun in the mid-1960s, resulted in the global eradication of the disease by 1980. WHO continues to be involved in infectious disease control, primarily in the developing world, with programs targeting malaria, HIV/AIDS, and tuberculosis, among others. It also runs programs to reduce illness and mortality that occur as a result of violence, accidents, lifestyle-associated illnesses such as diabetes, and poor health-care infrastructure.

WHO maintains a global alert and response system that coordinates information from member nations. In the event of a public health emergency or epidemic, it provides logistical support and coordinates international response to the emergency. The United States contributes to this effort through the CDC. The CDC carries out international monitoring and public health efforts, mainly in the service of protecting US public health in an increasingly connected world. Similarly, the European Union maintains a Health Security Committee that monitors disease outbreaks within its member countries and internationally, coordinating with WHO.

Emerging and Reemerging Infectious Diseases

Both WHO and some national public health agencies such as the CDC monitor and prepare for **emerging infectious diseases**. An emerging infectious disease is either new to the human population or has shown an increase in prevalence in the previous twenty years. Whether the disease is new or conditions have changed to cause an increase in frequency, its status as emerging implies the need to apply resources to understand and control its growing impact.

Emerging diseases may change their frequency gradually over time, or they may experience sudden epidemic growth. The importance of vigilance was made clear during the Ebola hemorrhagic fever epidemic in western Africa through 2014–2015. Although health experts had been aware of the Ebola virus since the 1970s, an outbreak on such a large scale had never happened before. Previous human epidemics had been small, isolated, and contained. Indeed, the gorilla and chimpanzee populations of western Africa had suffered far worse from Ebola than the human population. The pattern of small isolated human epidemics changed in 2014. Its high transmission rate, coupled with cultural practices for treatment of the dead and perhaps its emergence in an urban setting, caused the disease to spread rapidly, and thousands of people died. The international public health community responded with a large emergency effort to treat patients and contain the epidemic.

Emerging diseases are found in all countries, both developed and developing. Some nations are better equipped to deal with them. National and international public health agencies watch for epidemics like the Ebola outbreak in developing countries because those countries rarely have the health-care infrastructure and expertise to deal with large outbreaks effectively. Even with the support of international agencies, the systems in western Africa struggled to identify and care for the sick and control spread. In addition to the altruistic goal of saving lives and assisting nations lacking in resources, the global nature of transportation means that an outbreak anywhere can spread quickly to every corner of the planet. Managing an epidemic in one location—its source—is far easier than fighting it on many fronts.

Ebola is not the only disease that needs to be monitored in the global environment. In 2015, WHO set priorities on several emerging diseases that had a high probability of causing epidemics and that were poorly understood (and thus urgently required research and development efforts).

A **reemerging infectious disease** is a disease that is increasing in frequency after a previous period of decline. Its reemergence may be a result of changing conditions or old prevention regimes that are no longer working. Examples of such diseases are drug-resistant forms of tuberculosis, bacterial pneumonia, and malaria. Drug-resistant strains of the bacteria causing gonorrhea and syphilis are also

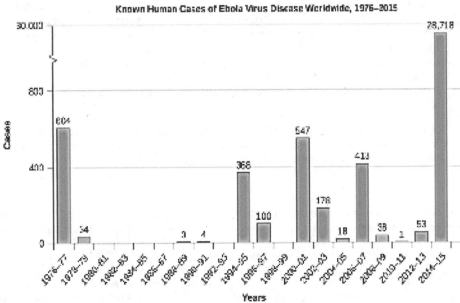

Figure 18 Even before the Ebola epidemic of 2014–15, Ebola was considered an emerging disease because of several smaller outbreaks between the mid-1990s and 2000s.

becoming more widespread, raising concerns of untreatable infections.

Some Emerging and Reemerging Infectious Diseases

Disease	Pathogen	Year Discovered	Affected Regions	Transmission
AIDS	HIV	1981	Worldwide	Contact with infected body fluids
Chikungunya fever	Chikungunya virus	1952	Africa, Asia, India; spreading to Europe and the Americas	Mosquito-borne
Ebola virus disease	Ebola virus	1976	Central and Western Africa	Contact with infected body fluids
H1N1 Influenza (swine flu)	H1N1 virus	2009	Worldwide	Droplet transmission
Lyme disease	Borrelia burgdorferi bacterium	1981	Northern hemisphere	From mammal reservoirs to humans by tick vectors
West Nile virus disease	West Nile virus	1937	Africa, Australia, Canada to Venezuela, Europe, Middle East, Western Asia	Mosquito-borne

Table 7

Circulatory System Infections

Under normal circumstances, the circulatory system and the blood should be sterile; the circulatory system has no normal microbiota. Because the system is closed, there are no easy portals of entry into the circulatory system for microbes. Those that are able to breach the body's physical barriers and enter the bloodstream encounter a host of circulating immune defenses, such as antibodies, complement proteins, phagocytes, and other immune cells. Microbes often gain access to the circulatory system through a break in the skin (e.g., wounds, needles, intravenous catheters, insect bites) or spread to the circulatory system from infections in other body sites. For example, microorganisms causing pneumonia or renal infection may enter the local circulation of the lung or kidney and spread from there throughout the circulatory network. Even the act of tooth brushing, which can cause small ruptures in the gums, may introduce bacteria into the circulatory system.

If microbes in the bloodstream are not quickly eliminated, they can spread rapidly throughout the body, leading to serious, even life-threatening infections. Various terms are used to describe conditions involving microbes in the circulatory system. The term **bacteremia** refers to bacteria in the blood. If bacteria are reproducing in the blood as they spread, this condition is called **septicemia**. The presence of viruses in the blood is called **viremia**. Microbial toxins can also be spread through the circulatory system, causing a condition termed **toxemia**.

Certain infections can cause inflammation in the heart and blood vessels. Inflammation of the endocardium, the inner lining of the heart, is called **endocarditis** and can result in damage to the heart valves severe enough to require surgical replacement.

Like the circulatory system, the lymphatic system does not have a normal microbiota, and the large numbers of immune cells typically eliminate transient microbes before they can establish an infection. Only microbes with an array of virulence factors are able to overcome these defenses and establish infection in the lymphatic system. However, when a localized infection begins to spread, the lymphatic system is often the first place the invading microbes can be detected. Infections in the lymphatic system also trigger an inflammatory response. Inflammation of lymphatic vessels, called **lymphangitis**, can produce visible red streaks under the skin. Inflammation in the lymph nodes can cause them to swell.

Bacterial Sepsis

Microbes and microbial toxins in the blood can trigger an inflammatory response so severe that the inflammation damages host tissues and organs more than the infection itself. This counterproductive immune response is called **systemic inflammatory response syndrome (SIRS),** and it can lead to the life-threatening condition known as **sepsis.** Sepsis is characterized by the production of excess cytokines that leads to classic signs of inflammation such as fever, vasodilation, and edema. In a patient with sepsis, the inflammatory response becomes dysregulated and disproportionate to the threat of infection. Critical organs such as the heart, lungs, liver, and kidneys become dysfunctional, resulting in increased heart and respiratory rates, and disorientation. If not treated promptly and effectively, patients with sepsis can develop shock and die. In these situations, it is often the immune response to the infection that results in the clinical signs and symptoms rather than the microbes themselves.

At low concentrations, pro-inflammatory chemicals such as interleukin 1 (IL-1) play important roles in the host's immune defenses. When they circulate systemically in larger amounts, however, the resulting immune response can be life threatening. IL-1 induces vasodilation (widening of blood vessels) and reduces the tight junctions between vascular endothelial cells, leading to widespread edema. As fluids move out of circulation into tissues, blood pressure begins to drop. If left unchecked, the blood pressure can fall below the level necessary to maintain proper kidney and respiratory functions, a condition known as **septic shock.** In addition, the excessive release of immune chemicals during the inflammatory response can lead to the formation of blood clots. The loss of blood pressure and occurrence of blood clots can result in multiple organ failure and death.

Bacteria are the most common pathogens associated with the development of sepsis, and septic shock. The most common infection associated with sepsis is bacterial pneumonia, accounting for about half of all cases, followed by intra-abdominal infections and urinary tract infections. Infections associated with superficial wounds, animal bites, and indwelling catheters may also lead to sepsis and septic shock.

These initially minor, localized infections can be caused by a wide range of different bacteria, including *Staphylococcus, Streptococcus, Pseudomonas, Pasteurella, Acinetobacter,* and members of the Enterobacteriaceae. However, if left untreated, infections by these gram-positive and gram-negative pathogens can potentially progress to sepsis, shock, and death.

Neonatal Sepsis

S. agalactiae, Group B streptococcus (GBS), is an encapsulated gram-positive bacterium that is the most common cause of neonatal meningitis leading to **neonatal sepsis**, a term that refers to sepsis occurring in babies up to 3 months of age. *S. agalactiae* can also cause meningitis in people of all ages and can be found in the urogenital and gastrointestinal microbiota of about 10–30% of humans.

Neonatal infection occurs as either early onset or late-onset disease. Early onset disease is defined as occurring in infants up to 7 days old. The infant initially becomes infected by *S. agalactiae* during childbirth, when the bacteria may be transferred from the mother's vagina. Incidence of early onset neonatal meningitis can be greatly reduced by giving intravenous antibiotics to the mother during labor.

Late-onset neonatal meningitis occurs in infants between 1 week and 3 months of age. Infants born to mothers with *S. agalactiae* in the urogenital tract have a higher risk of late-onset menigitis, but late-onset infections can be transmitted from sources other than the mother; often, the source of infection is unknown. Infants who are born prematurely (before 37 weeks of pregnancy) or to mothers who develop a fever also have a greater risk of contracting late-onset neonatal meningitis.

Signs and symptoms of early onset disease include temperature instability, apnea (cessation of breathing), bradycardia (slow heart rate), hypotension, difficulty feeding, irritability, and limpness. When asleep, the baby may be difficult to wake up. Symptoms of late-onset disease are more likely to include seizures, bulging fontanel (soft spot), stiff neck, hemiparesis (weakness on one side of the body), and opisthotonos (rigid body with arched back and head thrown backward).

Toxic Shock Syndrome

Toxemia associated with infections caused by *Staphylococcus aureus* can cause staphylococcal **toxic shock syndrome (TSS).** TSS may occur as a complication of other localized or systemic infections such as pneumonia, osteomyelitis, sinusitis, and skin wounds (surgical, traumatic, or burns). Those at highest risk for staphylococcal TSS are women with preexisting *S. aureus* colonization of the vagina who leave tampons, contraceptive sponges, diaphragms, or other devices in the vagina for longer than the recommended time.

Staphylococcal TSS is characterized by sudden onset of vomiting, diarrhea, myalgia, body temperature higher than 38.9 °C (102.0 °F), and rapid-onset hypotension with a systolic blood pressure less than 90 mm Hg for adults; a diffuse erythematous rash that leads to peeling and shedding skin 1 to 2 weeks after onset; and additional involvement of three or more organ systems. The mortality rate associated with staphylococcal TSS is less than 3% of cases.

Diagnosis of staphylococcal TSS is based on clinical signs, symptoms, serologic tests to confirm bacterial species, and the detection of toxin production from staphylococcal isolates. Cultures of skin and blood are often negative; less than 5% are positive in cases of staphylococcal TSS. Treatment for staphylococcal TSS includes decontamination, debridement, vasopressors to elevate blood pressure, and antibiotic therapy with clindamycin plus vancomycin or daptomycin pending susceptibility results.

Bacterial Endocarditis and Pericarditis

The endocardium is a tissue layer that lines the muscles and valves of the heart. This tissue can become infected by a variety of bacteria, including gram-positive cocci such as *Staphylococcus aureus*, viridans streptococci, and several others. The resulting inflammation is called **endocarditis**, which can be described as either acute or subacute. Causative agents typically enter the bloodstream during accidental or intentional breaches in the normal barrier defenses (e.g., dental procedures, body piercings, catheterization, wounds). Individuals with preexisting heart damage, prosthetic valves and other cardiac devices, and those with a history of rheumatic fever have a higher risk for endocarditis. This disease can rapidly destroy the heart valves and, if untreated, lead to death in just a few days.

In **subacute bacterial endocarditis**, heart valve damage occurs slowly over a period of months. During this time, blood clots form in the heart, and these protect the bacteria from phagocytes. The resulting damage to the heart, in part resulting from the immune response causing fibrosis of heart valves, can necessitate heart valve replacement. Outward signs of subacute endocarditis may include a fever.

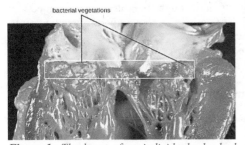

Figure 1 The heart of an individual who had subacute bacterial endocarditis of the mitral valve. Bacterial vegetations (tissue associated blood clots containing bacteria) are visible on the valve tissues. (credit: modification of work by Centers for Disease Control and Prevention)

Rheumatic Fever

Infections with *S. pyogenes* have a variety of manifestations and complications one of which is in the form of acute **rheumatic fever** (ARF), which can lead to rheumatic heart disease, thus impacting the circulatory system. Rheumatic fever occurs primarily in children a minimum of 2–3 weeks after an episode of untreated or inadequately treated pharyngitis (sore throat). At one time, rheumatic fever was a major killer of children in the US; today, however, it is rare in the US because of early diagnosis and treatment of streptococcal pharyngitis with antibiotics. In parts of the world where diagnosis and treatment are not readily available, acute rheumatic fever and rheumatic heart disease are still major causes of mortality in children.

Rheumatic fever is characterized by a variety of diagnostic signs and symptoms caused by immune-mediated damage resulting from a cross-reaction between patient antibodies to bacterial surface proteins and similar proteins found on cardiac, neuronal, and synovial tissues. Damage to the nervous tissue or joints, which leads to joint pain and swelling, is reversible. However, damage to heart valves can be irreversible and is worsened by repeated episodes of acute rheumatic fever, particularly during the first 3–5 years after the first rheumatic fever attack. The inflammation of the heart valves caused by cross-reacting antibodies leads to scarring and stiffness of the valve leaflets. This, in turn, produces a characteristic heart murmur. Patients who have previously developed rheumatic fever and who subsequently develop recurrent pharyngitis due to *S. pyogenes* are at high risk for a recurrent attacks of rheumatic fever.

Anthrax

The zoonotic disease **anthrax** is caused by *Bacillus anthracis*, a gram-positive, endospore-forming, facultative anaerobe. Anthrax mainly affects animals such as sheep, goats, cattle, and deer, but can be found in humans as well. Sometimes called wool sorter's disease, it is often transmitted to humans through contact with infected animals or animal products, such as wool or hides. However, exposure to *B. anthracis* can occur by other means, as the endospores are widespread in soils and can survive for long periods of time, sometimes for hundreds of years.

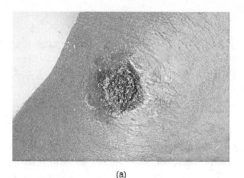
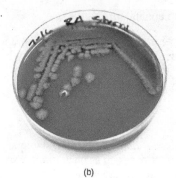

(a)   (b)

Figure 2 (a) Cutaneous anthrax is an infection of the skin by B. anthracis, which produces tissue-damaging exotoxins. Dead tissues accumulating in this nodule have produced a small black eschar. (b) Colonies of B. anthracis grown on sheep's blood agar. (credit a, b: modification of work by Centers for Disease Control and Prevention)

The vast majority of anthrax cases (95–99%) occur when anthrax endospores enter the body through abrasions of the skin.[8] This form of the disease is called cutaneous anthrax. It is characterized by the formation of a nodule on the skin; the cells within the nodule die, forming a mass of dead skin tissue. The localized infection can eventually lead to bacteremia and septicemia. If untreated, cutaneous anthrax can cause death in 20% of patients. Once in the skin tissues, *B. anthracis* endospores germinate and produce a capsule, which prevents the bacteria from being phagocytized, and two binary exotoxins that cause edema and tissue damage.

Less commonly, anthrax infections can be initiated through other portals of entry such as the digestive tract (gastrointestinal anthrax) or respiratory tract (pulmonary anthrax or inhalation anthrax). Typically, cases of noncutaneous anthrax are more difficult to treat than the cutaneous form. The mortality rate for gastrointestinal anthrax can be up to 40%, even with treatment. Inhalation anthrax, which occurs when anthrax spores are inhaled, initially causes influenza-like symptoms, but mortality rates are approximately 45% in treated individuals and 85% in those not treated. A relatively new form of the disease, injection anthrax, has been reported in Europe in intravenous drug users; it occurs when drugs are contaminated with *B. anthracis*. Patients with injection anthrax show signs and symptoms of severe soft tissue infection that differ clinically from cutaneous anthrax. This often delays diagnosis and treatment, and leads to a high mortality rate.

B. anthracis colonies on blood agar have a rough texture and serrated edges that eventually form an undulating band. Broad spectrum antibiotics such as penicillin, erythromycin, and tetracycline are often effective treatments.

Unfortunately, *B. anthracis* has been used as a biological weapon and remains on the United Nations' list of potential agents of bioterrorism. Over a period of several months in 2001, a number of letters were mailed to members of the news media and the United States Congress. As a result, 11 individuals developed cutaneous anthrax and another 11 developed inhalation anthrax. Those infected included recipients of the letters, postal workers, and two other individuals. Five of those infected with pulmonary anthrax died. The anthrax spores had been carefully prepared to aerosolize, showing that the perpetrator had a high level of expertise in microbiology.

A vaccine is available to protect individuals from anthrax. However, unlike most routine vaccines, the current anthrax vaccine is unique in both its formulation and the protocols dictating who receives it. The vaccine is administered through five intramuscular injections over a period of 18 months, followed by annual boosters. The US Food and Drug Administration (FDA) has only approved administration of the vaccine prior to exposure for at-risk adults, such as individuals who work with anthrax in a laboratory, some individuals who handle animals or animal products (e.g., some veterinarians), and some members of the United States military. The vaccine protects against cutaneous and inhalation anthrax using cell-free filtrates of microaerophilic cultures of an avirulent, nonencapsulated strain of *B. anthracis*. The FDA has not approved the vaccine for routine use *after* exposure to anthrax, but if there were ever an anthrax emergency in the United States, patients could be given anthrax vaccine after exposure to help prevent disease.

Gas Gangrene

Traumatic injuries or certain medical conditions, such as diabetes, can cause damage to blood vessels that interrupts blood flow to a region of the body. When blood flow is interrupted, tissues begin to die, creating an anaerobic environment in which anaerobic bacteria can thrive. This condition is called ischemia. Endospores of the anaerobic bacterium ***Clostridium perfringens*** (along with a number of other *Clostridium* spp. from the gut) can readily germinate in ischemic tissues and colonize the anaerobic tissues.

The resulting infection, called **gas gangrene**, is characterized by rapidly spreading myonecrosis (death of muscle tissue). The patient experiences a sudden onset of excruciating pain at the infection site and the rapid development of a foul-smelling wound containing gas bubbles and a thin, yellowish discharge tinged with a small amount of blood. As the infection progresses, edema and cutaneous blisters containing bluish-purple fluid form. The infected tissue becomes liquefied and begins sloughing off. The margin between necrotic and healthy tissue often advances several inches per hour even with antibiotic therapy. Septic shock and organ failure frequently accompany gas gangrene; when patients develop sepsis, the mortality rate is greater than 50%.

Gas gangrene is initially diagnosed based on the pres-

gas pockets

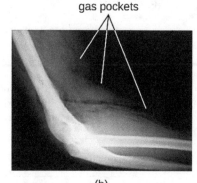

(a)   (b)

Figure 3 (a) In this image of a patient with gas gangrene, note the bluish-purple discoloration around the bicep and the irregular margin of the discolored tissue indicating the spread of infection. (b) A radiograph of the arm shows a darkening in the tissue, which indicates the presence of gas. (credit a, b: modification of work by Aggelidakis J, Lasithiotakis K, Topalidou A, Koutroumpas J, Kouvidis G, and Katonis P)

ence of the clinical signs and symptoms described earlier in this section. Diagnosis can be confirmed through Gram stain and anaerobic cultivation of wound exudate (drainage) and tissue samples on blood agar. Treatment typically involves surgical debridement of any necrotic tissue; advanced cases may require amputation. Surgeons may also use vacuum-assisted closure (VAC), a surgical technique in which vacuum-assisted drainage is used to remove blood or serous fluid from a wound or surgical site to speed recovery. The most common antibiotic treatments include penicillin G and clindamycin. Some cases are also treated with hyperbaric oxygen therapy because *Clostridium* spp. are incapable of surviving in oxygen-rich environments.

Lyme Disease

Lyme disease is caused by the spiral shaped bacterium *Borrelia burgdorferi* that is transmitted by the bite of a hard-bodied, black-legged *Ixodes* tick. *I. scapularis* is the biological vector transmitting *B. burgdorferi* in the eastern and north-central US and *I. pacificus* transmits *B. burgdorferi* in the western US . Different species of *Ixodes* ticks are responsible for *B. burgdorferi* transmission in Asia and Europe. In the US, Lyme disease is the most commonly reported vectorborne illness. In 2014, it was the fifth most common Nationally Notifiable disease.

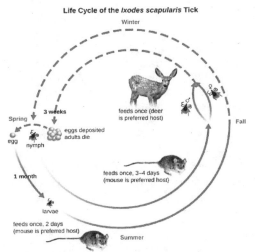

Figure 4 *This image shows the 2-year life cycle of the black-legged tick, the biological vector of Lyme disease. (credit "mouse": modification of work by George Shuklin)*

Ixodes ticks have complex life cycles and deer, mice, and even birds can act as reservoirs. Over 2 years, the ticks pass through four developmental stages and require a blood meal from a host at each stage. In the spring, tick eggs hatch into six-legged larvae. These larvae do not carry *B. burgdorferi* initially. They may acquire the spirochete when they take their first blood meal (typically from a mouse). The larvae then overwinter and molt into eight-legged nymphs in the following spring. Nymphs take blood meals primarily from small rodents, but may also feed on humans, burrowing into the skin. The feeding period can last several days to a week, and it typically takes 24 hours for an infected nymph to transmit enough *B. burgdorferi* to cause infection in a human host. Nymphs ultimately mature into male and female adult ticks, which tend to feed on larger animals like deer or, occasionally, humans. The adults then mate and produce eggs to continue the cycle.

The symptoms of Lyme disease follow three stages: early localized, early disseminated, and late stage. During the early-localized stage, approximately 70%–80% of cases may be characterized by a bull's-eye rash, called erythema migrans, at the site of the initial tick bite. The rash forms 3 to 30 days after the tick bite (7 days is the average) and may also be warm to the touch. This diagnostic sign is often overlooked if the tick bite occurs on the scalp or another less visible location. Other early symptoms include flu-like symptoms such as malaise, headache, fever, and muscle stiffness. If the patient goes untreated, the second early-disseminated stage of the disease occurs days to weeks later. The symptoms at this stage may include severe headache, neck stiffness,

facial paralysis, arthritis, and carditis. The late-stage manifestations of the disease may occur years after exposure. Chronic inflammation causes damage that can eventually cause severe arthritis, meningitis, encephalitis, and altered mental states. The disease may be fatal if untreated.

A presumptive diagnosis of Lyme disease can be made based solely on the presence of a bull's-eye rash at the site of infection, if it is present, in addition to other associated symptoms. In addition, indirect immunofluorescent antibody (IFA) labeling can be used to visualize bacteria from blood or skin biopsy specimens. Serological tests like ELISA can also be used to detect serum antibodies produced in response to infection. During the early stage of infection (about 30 days), antibacterial drugs such as amoxicillin and doxycycline are effective. In the later stages, penicillin G, chloramphenicol, or ceftriaxone can be given intravenously.

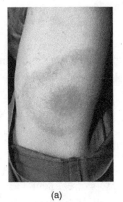 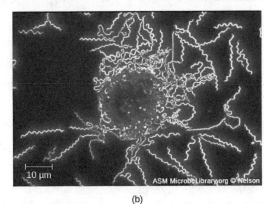

(a)   (b)

Figure 5 *(a) A characteristic bull's eye rash of Lyme disease forms at the site of a tick bite. (b) A darkfield micrograph shows Borrelia burgdorferi, the causative agent of Lyme disease. (credit a: modification of work by Centers for Disease Control and Prevention; credit b: modification of work by American Society for Microbiology)*

Foodborne and Waterborne Illnesses

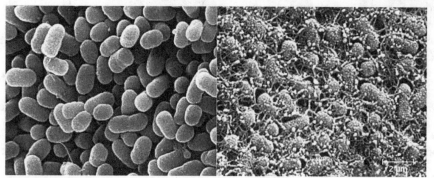

Figure 1 E. coli O157:H7 causes serious foodborne illness. Curli fibers (adhesive surface fibers that are part of the extracellular matrix) help these bacteria adhere to surfaces and form biofilms. Pictured are two groups of cells, curli non-producing cells (left) and curli producing cells (right). (credit left, right: modification of work by USDA)

Gastrointestinal (GI) diseases are so common that, unfortunately, most people have had first-hand experience with the unpleasant symptoms, such as diarrhea, vomiting, and abdominal discomfort. The causes of gastrointestinal illness can vary widely, but such diseases can be grouped into two categories: those caused by infection (the growth of a pathogen in the GI tract) or intoxication (the presence of a microbial toxin in the GI tract).

Foodborne pathogens like *Escherichia coli* O157:H7 are among the most common sources of gastrointestinal disease. Contaminated food and water have always posed a health risk for humans, but in today's global economy, outbreaks can occur on a much larger scale. *E. coli* O157:H7 is a potentially deadly strain of *E. coli* with a history of contaminating meat and produce that are not properly processed. The source of an *E. coli* O157:H7 outbreak can be difficult to trace, especially if the contaminated food is processed in a foreign country. Once the source is identified, authorities may issue recalls of the contaminated food products, but by then there are typically numerous cases of food poisoning, some of them fatal.

General Signs and Symptoms of Oral and GI Disease

Despite numerous defense mechanisms that protect against infection, all parts of the digestive tract can become sites of infection or intoxication. The term food poisoning is sometimes used as a catch-all for GI infections and intoxications, but not all forms of GI disease originate with foodborne pathogens or toxins.

Infections and intoxications of the lower GI tract often produce symptoms such as nausea, vomiting, diarrhea, aches, and fever. In some cases, vomiting and diarrhea may cause severe dehydration and other complications that can become serious or fatal. Various clinical terms are used to describe gastrointestinal symptoms. For example, **gastritis** is an inflammation of the stomach lining that results in swelling and **enteritis** refers to inflammation of the intestinal mucosa. When the inflammation involves both the stomach lining and the intestinal lining, the condition is called **gastroenteritis**. Inflammation of the liver is called **hepatitis**. Inflammation of the colon, called **colitis,** commonly occurs in cases of food intoxication. Because an inflamed colon does not reabsorb water as effectively as it normally does, stools become watery, causing diarrhea. Damage to the epithelial cells of the colon can also cause bleeding and excess mucus to appear in watery stools, a condition called **dysentery**.

Infection and Intoxication

A wide range of gastrointestinal diseases are caused by bacterial contamination of food. Recall that foodborne disease can arise from either **infection** or **intoxication**. In both cases, bacterial toxins are typically responsible for producing disease signs and symptoms. The distinction lies in where the toxins are produced. In an infection, the microbial agent is ingested, colonizes the gut, and then produces toxins that damage host cells. In an intoxication, bacteria produce toxins in the food before it is ingested. In either case, the toxins cause damage to the cells lining the gastrointestinal tract, typically the colon. This leads to the common signs and symptoms of diarrhea or watery stool and abdominal cramps, or the more severe dysentery. Symptoms of foodborne diseases also often include nausea and vomiting, which are mechanisms the body uses to expel the toxic materials.

Most bacterial gastrointestinal illness is short-lived and self-limiting; however, loss of fluids due to severe diarrheal illness can lead to dehydration that can, in some cases, be fatal without proper treatment. Oral rehydration therapy with electrolyte solutions is an essential aspect of treatment for most patients with GI disease, especially in children and infants.

Fecal Coliform bacteria

Community water supplies and food processing plants are challenged with keeping food and water safe for consumers. Since human and animal feces are the most common source of food borne pathogens, food and water are often tested for exposure to fecal material. This is done by screening food and water for **fecal coliform bacteria**. Fecal coliforms are gram negative bacteria that produce acid and gas on lactose, aerobic or facultative anaerobic and do not form endospores. *E. coli* is a fecal coliform and would be present in the case of fecal contamination. Fecal coliforms are indicators of fecal contamination and therefore the possibility of contamination by many of the potential pathogens found in feces.

E. coli Infections

The gram-negative rod *Escherichia coli* is a common member of the normal microbiota of the colon and a fecal coliform. Although the vast majority of *E. coli* strains are helpful commensal bacteria, some can be pathogenic and may cause dangerous diarrheal disease. The pathogenic strains have additional virulence factors such as type 1 fimbriae that promote colonization of the colon or may produce toxins. These virulence factors can be acquired through horizontal gene transfer.

These bacteria can be spread from person to person, although they are often acquired through contaminated food or water. There are six recognized pathogenic groups of *E. coli*, but we will focus here on the four that are most commonly transmitted through food and water.

Enterotoxigenic *E. coli* (ETEC), also known as **traveler's diarrhea**, causes diarrheal illness and is common in less developed countries. In Mexico, ETEC infection is called Montezuma's Revenge. Following ingestion of contaminated food or water, infected individuals develop a watery diarrhea, abdominal cramps, malaise (a feeling of being unwell), and a low fever. ETEC produces a heat-stable enterotoxin similar to cholera toxin, and adhesins called colonization factors that help the bacteria to attach to the intestinal wall.

Enteroinvasive *E. coli* (EIEC) is very similar to shigellosis, including its pathogenesis of intracellular invasion into intestinal epithelial tissue. This bacterium carries a large plasmid that is involved in epithelial cell penetration. The illness is usually self-limiting, with symptoms including watery diarrhea, chills, cramps, malaise, fever, and dysentery.

Enteropathogenic *E. coli* (EPEC) can cause a potentially fatal diarrhea, especially in infants and those in less developed countries. Fever, vomiting, and diarrhea can lead to severe dehydration.

The most dangerous strains are **enterohemorrhagic *E. coli* (EHEC),** which are the strains capable of causing epidemics. In particular, the **strain O157:H7** has been responsible for several recent outbreaks. EHEC can cause disease ranging from relatively mild to life-threatening. Symptoms include bloody diarrhea with severe cramping, but no fever. Although it is often self-limiting, it can lead to hemorrhagic colitis and profuse bleeding. One serious complication results from damage to the blood vessels in the kidneys and is called **hemolytic uremic syndrome (HUS).**

Some Pathogenic Groups of *E. coli*		
Group	**Signs and Symptoms**	**Treatment**
Enterotoxigenic *E. coli* (ETEC)	Relatively mild, watery diarrhea	Self-limiting; if needed, fluoroquinolones, doxycycline, rifaximin, TMP/SMZ; antibiotic resistance is a problem
Enteroinvasive *E. coli* (EIEC)	Relatively mild, watery diarrhea; dysentery or inflammatory colitis may occur	Supportive therapy only; antibiotics not recommended
Enteropathogenic *E. coli* (EPEC)	Severe fever, vomiting, nonbloody diarrhea, dehydration; potentially fatal	Self-limiting; if needed, fluoroquinolones, doxycycline, rifaximin (TMP/SMZ); antibiotic resistance is a problem
Enterohemorrhagic *E. coli* (EHEC)	May be mild or very severe; bloody diarrhea; may result in HUS	Antibiotics are not recommended due to the risk of HUS

Table 1

Salmonellosis

Salmonella gastroenteritis, also called **salmonellosis,** is caused by the rod-shaped, gram-negative bacterium *Salmonella*. Two species, *S. enterica* and *S. bongori*, cause disease in humans, but *S. enterica* is the most common. The most common serotypes of *S. enterica* are Enteritidis and Typhi. We will discuss typhoid fever caused by serotypes Typhi and Paratyphi A separately. Here, we will focus on salmonellosis caused by other serotypes.

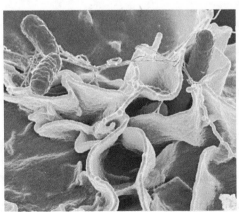

Figure 2 Salmonella entering an intestinal epithelial cell by reorganizing the host cell's cytoskeleton via the trigger mechanism. (credit: modification of work by National Institutes for Health)

Salmonella is a part of the normal intestinal microbiota of many individuals. However, salmonellosis is caused by exogenous agents, and infection can occur depending on the serotype, size of the inoculum, and overall health of the host. Infection is caused by ingestion of contaminated food, handling of eggshells, or exposure to certain animals. *Salmonella* is part of poultry's microbiota, so exposure to raw eggs and raw poultry can increase the risk of infection. Handwashing and cooking foods thoroughly greatly reduce the risk of transmission. *Salmonella* bacteria can survive freezing for extended periods but cannot survive high temperatures.

Once the bacteria are ingested, they multiply within the intestines and penetrate the epithelial mucosal cells via M cells where they continue to grow. They trigger inflammatory processes and the hypersecretion of fluids. Once inside the body, they can persist inside the phagosomes of macrophages. *Salmonella* can cross the epithelial cell membrane and enter the bloodstream and lymphatic system. Some strains of *Salmonella* also produce an enterotoxin (exotoxin that affects the intestines) that can cause an intoxication.

Infected individuals develop fever, nausea, abdominal cramps, vomiting, headache, and diarrhea. These signs and symptoms generally last a few days to a week. According to the Centers for Disease Control and Prevention (CDC), there are 1,000,000 cases annually, with 380 deaths each year.[5] However, because the disease is usually self-limiting, many cases are not reported to doctors and the overall incidence may be underreported. Diagnosis involves culture followed by serotyping and DNA fingerprinting if needed. Positive results are reported to the CDC. When an unusual serotype is detected, samples are sent to the CDC for further analysis. Serotyping is important for determining treatment. Oral rehydration therapy is commonly used. Antibiotics are only recommended for serious cases. When antibiotics are needed, as in immunocompromised patients, fluoroquinolones, third-generation cephalosporins, and ampicillin are recommended. Antibiotic resistance is a serious concern.

Staphylococcal Food Poisoning

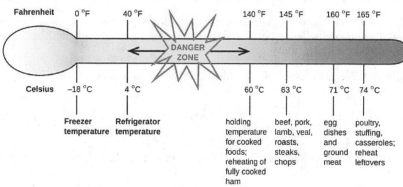

Figure 3 *This figure indicates safe internal temperatures associated with the refrigeration, cooking, and reheating of different foods. Temperatures above refrigeration and below the minimum cooking temperature may allow for microbial growth, increasing the likelihood of foodborne disease. (credit: modification of work by USDA)*

Staphylococcal food poisoning is one form of food intoxication. When *Staphylococcus aureus* grows in food, it may produce enterotoxins that, when ingested, can cause symptoms such as nausea, diarrhea, cramping, and vomiting within one to six hours. In some severe cases, it may cause headache, dehydration, and changes in blood pressure and heart rate. Signs and symptoms resolve within 24 to 48 hours. *S. aureus* is often associated with a variety of raw or undercooked and cooked foods including meat (e.g., canned meat, ham, and sausages) and dairy products (e.g., cheeses, milk, and butter). It is also commonly found on hands and can be transmitted to prepared foods through poor hygiene, including poor handwashing and the use of contaminated food preparation surfaces, such as cutting boards. The greatest risk is for food left at a temperature below 60 °C (140 °F), which allows the bacteria to grow. Cooked foods should generally be reheated to at least 60 °C (140 °F) for safety and most raw meats should be cooked to even higher internal temperatures.

There are at least 21 *Staphylococcal* enterotoxins and *Staphylococcal* enterotoxin-like toxins that can cause food intoxication. The enterotoxins are proteins that are resistant to low pH, allowing them to pass through the stomach. They are heat stable and are not destroyed by boiling at 100 °C. Even though the bacterium itself may be killed, the enterotoxins alone can cause vomiting and diarrhea, although the mechanisms are not fully understood.

The rapid onset of signs and symptoms helps to diagnose this foodborne illness. Because the bacterium does not need to be present for the toxin to cause symptoms, diagnosis is confirmed by identifying the toxin in a food sample or in biological specimens (feces or vomitus) from the patient. Serological techniques, including ELISA, can also be used to identify the toxin in food samples.

The condition generally resolves relatively quickly, within 24 hours, without treatment. In some cases, supportive treatment in a hospital may be needed.

Hepatitis A

Hepatitis is a general term meaning inflammation of the liver, which can have a variety of causes. In some cases, the cause is viral infection. There are five main hepatitis viruses that are clinically significant: hepatitis viruses A (HAV), B (HBV), C (HCV), D, (HDV) and E (HEV). Note that other viruses, such as Epstein-Barr virus (EBV), yellow fever, and cytomegalovirus (CMV) can also cause hepatitis.

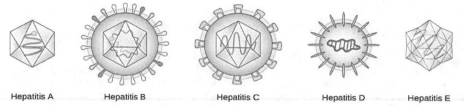

Figure 4 *Five main types of viruses cause hepatitis. HAV is a non-enveloped ssRNA(+) virus and is a member of the picornavirus family (Baltimore Group IV). HBV is a dsDNA enveloped virus, replicates using reverse transcriptase, and is a member of the hepadnavirus family (Baltimore Group VII). HCV is an enveloped ssRNA(+) virus and is a member of the flavivirus family (Baltimore Group IV). HDV is an enveloped ssRNA(–) that is circular (Baltimore Group V).*

Although the five hepatitis viruses differ, they can cause some similar signs and symptoms because they all have an affinity for hepatocytes (liver cells). **HAV** and HEV can be contracted through ingestion while HBV, HCV, and HDV are transmitted by parenteral contact. It is possible for individuals to become long term or chronic carriers of hepatitis viruses.

Hepatitis A is a vaccine-preventable, communicable disease of the liver caused by the hepatitis A virus (HAV). It is usually transmitted person-to-person through the fecal-oral route or consumption of contaminated food or water. Hepatitis A is a self-limited disease that does not result in chronic infection. Most adults with hepatitis A have symptoms, including fatigue, low appetite, stomach pain, nausea, and jaundice, that usually resolve within 2 months of infection; most children less than 6 years of age do not have symptoms or have an unrecognized infection. Antibodies produced in response to hepatitis A infection last for life and protect against reinfection. The best way to prevent hepatitis A infection is to get vaccinated.

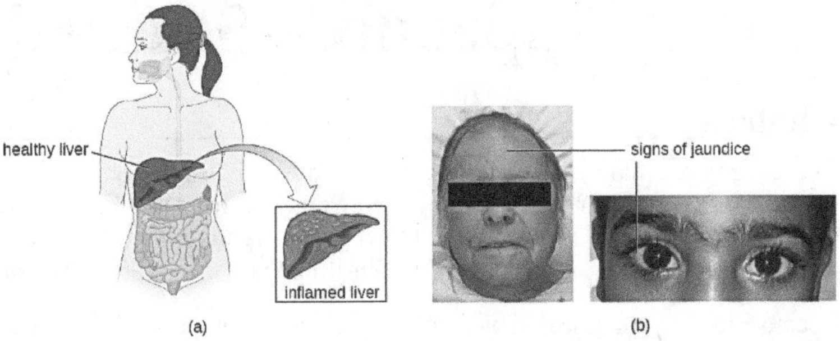

Gastroenteritis Caused by Noroviruses

Several strains of **Norovirus** can cause gastroenteritis. There are millions of cases a year, predominately in infants, young children, and the elderly. These viruses are easily transmitted and highly contagious. They are known for causing widespread infections in groups of people in confined spaces, such as on cruise ships. The viruses can be transmitted through direct contact, through touching contaminated surfaces, and through contaminated food. Because the virus is not killed by disinfectants used at standard concentrations for killing bacteria, the risk of transmission remains high, even after cleaning.

Figure 5 (a) Hepatitis is inflammation of the liver resulting from a variety of root causes. It can cause jaundice. (b) Jaundice is characterized by yellowing of the skin, mucous membranes, and sclera of the eyes. (credit b left: modification of work by James Heilman, MD; credit b right: modification of work by "Sab3e-l3eish"/Wikimedia Commons)

The signs and symptoms of norovirus infection are watery diarrhea, mild cramps, and fever. Additionally, these viruses sometimes cause projectile vomiting. The illness is usually relatively mild, develops 12 to 48 hours after exposure, and clears within a couple of days without treatment. However, dehydration may occur.

No medications are available, but the illness is usually self-limiting. Rehydration therapy and electrolyte replacement may be used. Good hygiene, hand washing, and careful food preparation reduce the risk of infection.

Clostridium botulinum - Botulism

Botulism is a rare but frequently fatal illness caused by intoxication by botulism neurotoxin (BoNT) produced by *Clostridium botulinum*. It can occur either as the result of an infection by *C. botulinum*, in which case the bacteria produce BoNT *in vivo*, or as the result of a direct introduction of BoNT into tissues.

Infection and production of BoNT *in vivo* can result in wound botulism, infant botulism, and adult intestinal toxemia. Wound botulism typically occurs when *C. botulinum* is introduced directly into a wound after a traumatic injury, deep puncture wound, or injection site. Infant botulism, which occurs in infants younger than 1 year of age, and adult intestinal toxemia, which occurs in immunocompromised adults, results from ingesting *C. botulinum* endospores in food. The endospores germinate in the body, resulting in the production of BoNT in the intestinal tract.

Intoxications occur when BoNT is produced outside the body and then introduced directly into the body through food (foodborne botulism), air (inhalation botulism), or a clinical procedure (iatrogenic botulism). Foodborne botulism, the most common of these forms, occurs when BoNT is produced in contaminated food and then ingested along with the food. Inhalation botulism is rare because BoNT is unstable as an aerosol and does not occur in nature; however, it can be produced in the laboratory and was used (unsuccessfully) as a bioweapon by terrorists in Japan in the 1990s. A few cases of accidental inhalation botulism have also occurred. Iatrogenic botulism is also rare; it is associated with injections of BoNT used for cosmetic purposes.

When BoNT enters the bloodstream in the gastrointestinal tract, wound, or lungs, it is transferred to the neuromuscular junctions of motor neurons where it binds irreversibly to presynaptic membranes and prevents the release of acetylcholine from the presynaptic terminal of motor neurons into the neuromuscular junction. The consequence of preventing acetylcholine release is the loss of muscle activity, leading to muscle relaxation and eventually paralysis.

If BoNT is absorbed through the gastrointestinal tract, early symptoms of botulism include blurred vision, drooping eyelids, difficulty swallowing, abdominal cramps, nausea, vomiting, constipation, or possibly diarrhea. This is followed by progressive flaccid paralysis, a gradual weakening and loss of control over the muscles. A patient's experience can be particularly terrifying, because hearing remains normal, consciousness is not lost, and he or she is fully aware of the progression of his or her condition. In infants, notable signs of botulism include weak cry, decreased ability to suckle, and hypotonia (limpness of head or body). Eventually, botulism ends in death from respiratory failure caused by the progressive paralysis of the muscles of the upper airway, diaphragm, and chest.

Botulism is treated with an antitoxin specific for BoNT. If administered in time, the antitoxin stops the progression of paralysis but does not reverse it. Once the antitoxin has been administered, the patient will slowly regain neurological function, but this may take several weeks or months, depending on the severity of the case. During recovery, patients generally must remain hospitalized and receive breathing assistance through a ventilator.

Appendix – Selected Microorganisms

Cholera

The gastrointestinal disease **cholera** is a serious infection often associated with poor sanitation, especially following natural disasters, because it is spread through contaminated water and food that has not been heated to temperatures high enough to kill the bacteria. It is caused by *Vibrio cholerae* serotype O1, a gram-negative, flagellated bacterium in the shape of a curved rod (vibrio). According to the CDC, cholera causes an estimated 3 to 5 million cases and 100,000 deaths each year.

Because *V. cholerae* is killed by stomach acid, relatively large doses are needed for a few microbial cells to survive to reach the intestines and cause infection. The motile cells travel through the mucous layer of the intestines, where they attach to epithelial cells and release cholera enterotoxin. Diarrhea is so profuse that it is often called "rice water stool," and patients are placed on cots with a hole in them to monitor the fluid loss.

Cholera may be self-limiting and treatment involves rehydration and electrolyte replenishment. Although antibiotics are not typically needed, they can be used for severe or disseminated disease. Tetracyclines are recommended, but doxycycline, erythromycin, ofloxacin, ciprofloxacin, and TMP/SMZ may be used. Recent evidence suggests that azithromycin is also a good first-line antibiotic. Good sanitation—including appropriate sewage treatment, clean supplies for cooking, and purified drinking water—is important to prevent infection.

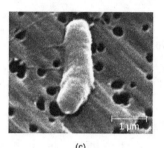

(a)   (b)   (c)

Figure 1 (a) Outbreaks of cholera often occur in areas with poor sanitation or after natural disasters that compromise sanitation infrastructure. (b) At a cholera treatment center in Haiti, patients are receiving intravenous fluids to combat the dehydrating effects of this disease. They often lie on a cot with a hole in it and a bucket underneath to allow for monitoring of fluid loss. (c) This scanning electron micrograph shows Vibrio cholera. (credit a, b: modification of work by Centers for Disease Control and Prevention; credit c: modification of work by Janice Carr, Centers for Disease Control and Prevention)

Clostridium difficile

Clostridium difficile is a gram-positive rod that can be a commensal bacterium as part of the normal microbiota of healthy individuals. When the normal microbiota is disrupted by long-term antibiotic use, it can allow the overgrowth of this bacterium, resulting in **antibiotic-associated diarrhea** caused by *C. difficile*. Antibiotic-associated diarrhea can also be considered a nosocomial disease. Patients at the greatest risk of *C. difficile* infection are those who are immunocompromised, have been in health-care settings for extended periods, are older, have recently taken antibiotics, have had gastrointestinal procedures done, or use proton pump inhibitors, which reduce stomach acidity and allow proliferation of *C. difficile*. Because this species can form endospores, it can survive for extended periods of time in the environment under harsh conditions and is a considerable concern in health-care settings.

The first step of conventional treatment is to stop antibiotic use, and then to provide supportive therapy with electrolyte replacement and fluids. A newer approach to treatment, known as a fecal transplant, focuses on restoring the microbiota of the gut in order to combat the infection. In this procedure, a healthy individual donates a stool sample, which is mixed with saline and transplanted to the recipient via colonoscopy, endoscopy, sigmoidoscopy, or enema. It has been reported that this procedure has greater than 90% success in resolving *C. difficile* infections.

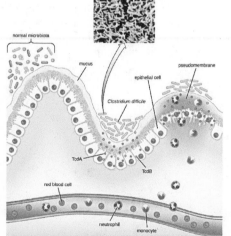

Figure 2 Clostridium difficile is able to colonize the mucous membrane of the colon when the normal microbiota is disrupted. The toxins TcdA and TcdB trigger an immune response, with neutrophils and monocytes migrating from the bloodstream to the site of infection. Over time, inflammation and dead cells contribute to the development of a pseudomembrane. (credit micrograph: modification of work by Janice Carr, Centers for Disease Control and Prevention)

Streptococcal Infections

A common upper respiratory infection, streptococcal pharyngitis (strep throat) is caused by *Streptococcus pyogenes*. This gram-positive bacterium appears as chains of cocci. Rebecca Lancefield serologically classified streptococci in the 1930s using carbohydrate antigens from the bacterial cell walls. *S. pyogenes* is the sole member of the Lancefield group A streptococci and is often referred to as GAS, or group A strep.

Similar to streptococcal infections of the skin, the mucosal membranes of the pharynx are damaged by the release of a variety of exoenzymes and exotoxins by this extracellular pathogen. Many strains of *S. pyogenes* can degrade connective tissues by using hyaluronidase, collagenase and streptokinase. Streptokinase activates plasmin, which leads to degradation of fibrin and, in turn, dissolution of blood clots, which assists in the spread of the pathogen. Released toxins include streptolysins that can destroy red and white blood cells. The classic signs of streptococcal pharyngitis are a fever higher than 38 °C (100.4 °F); intense pharyngeal pain; erythema associated with pharyngeal inflammation; and swollen, dark-red palatine tonsils, often dotted with patches of pus; and petechiae (microcapillary hemorrhages) on the soft or hard palate (roof of the mouth). The submandibular lymph nodes beneath the angle of the jaw are also often swollen during strep throat.

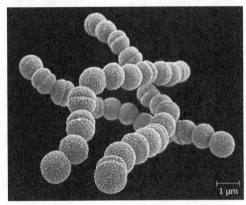

Figure 3 This scanning electron micrograph of *Streptococcus pyogenes* shows the characteristic cellular phenotype resembling chains of cocci. (credit: modification of work by U.S. Centers for Disease Control and Prevention - Medical Illustrator)

S. pyogenes can be easily spread by direct contact or droplet transmission through coughing and sneezing. The disease can be diagnosed quickly using a rapid enzyme immunoassay for the group A antigen. However, due to a significant rate of false-negative results (up to 30%[4]), culture identification is still the gold standard to confirm pharyngitis due to *S. pyogenes*. *S. pyogenes* can be identified as a catalase-negative, beta hemolytic bacterium that is susceptible to 0.04 units of bacitracin. Antibiotic resistance is limited for this bacterium, so most β-lactams remain effective; oral amoxicillin and intramuscular penicillin G are those most commonly prescribed.

Sequelae of S. pyogenes *Infections*

One reason strep throat infections are aggressively treated with antibiotics is because they can lead to serious sequelae, later clinical consequences of a primary infection. It is estimated that 1%–3% of untreated *S. pyogenes* infections can be followed by nonsuppurative (without the production of pus) sequelae that develop 1–3 weeks after the acute infection has resolved. Two such sequelae are acute rheumatic fever and acute glomerulonephritis.

Acute **rheumatic fever** can follow pharyngitis caused by specific rheumatogenic strains of *S. pyogenes* (strains 1, 3, 5, 6, and 18). The most serious and lethal clinical manifestation of rheumatic fever is damage to and inflammation of the heart (carditis).

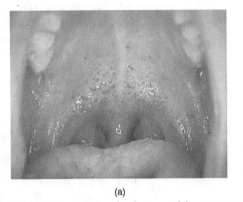
(a)

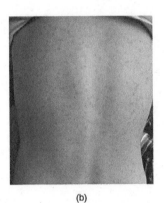
(b)

Figure 4 Streptococcal infections of the respiratory tract may cause localized pharyngitis or systemic signs and symptoms. (a) The characteristic appearance of strep throat: bright red arches of inflammation with the presence of dark-red spots (petechiae). (b) Scarlet fever presents as a rash on the skin. (credit a: modification of work by Centers for Disease Control and Prevention; credit b: modification of work by Alicia Williams)

Tuberculosis

Tuberculosis (TB) is one of the deadliest infectious diseases in human history. Although tuberculosis infection rates in the United States are extremely low, the CDC estimates that about one-third of the world's population is infected with *Mycobacterium tuberculosis*, the causal organism of TB, with 9.6 million new TB cases and 1.5 million deaths worldwide in 2014.

M. tuberculosis is an acid-fast, high G + C, gram-positive, nonspore-forming rod. Its cell wall is rich in waxy mycolic acids, which make the cells impervious to polar molecules. It also causes these organisms to grow slowly. *M. tuberculosis* causes a chronic granulomatous disease that can infect any area of the body, although it is typically associated with the lungs. *M. tuberculosis* is spread by inhalation of respiratory droplets or aerosols from an infected person. The infectious dose of *M. tuberculosis* is only 10 cells.

After inhalation, the bacteria enter the alveoli. The cells are phagocytized by macrophages but can survive and multiply within these phagocytes because of the protection by the waxy mycolic acid in their cell walls. If not eliminated by macrophages, the infection can progress, causing an inflammatory response and an accumulation of neutrophils and macrophages in the area. Several weeks or months may pass before an immunological response is mounted by T cells and B cells. Eventually, the lesions in the alveoli become walled off, forming small round lesions called **tubercles**. Bacteria continue to be released into the center of the tubercles and the chronic immune response results in tissue damage and induction of apoptosis (programmed host-cell death) in a process called liquefaction. This creates a caseous center, or air pocket, where the aerobic *M. tuberculosis* can grow and multiply. Tubercles may eventually rupture and bacterial cells can invade pulmonary capillaries; from there, bacteria can spread through the bloodstream to other organs, a condition known as miliary tuberculosis. The rupture of tubercles also facilitates transmission of the bacteria to other individuals via droplet aerosols that exit the body in coughs. Because these droplets can be very small and stay aloft for a long time, special precautions are necessary when caring for patients with TB, such as the use of face masks and negative-pressure ventilation and filtering systems.

Eventually, most lesions heal to form calcified Ghon complexes. These structures are visible on chest radiographs and are a useful diagnostic feature. But even after the disease has apparently ended, viable bacteria remain sequestered in these locations. Release of these organisms at a later time can produce reactivation tuberculosis (or secondary TB). This is mainly observed in people with alcoholism, the elderly, or in otherwise immunocompromised individuals.

Because TB is a chronic disease, chemotherapeutic treatments often continue for months or years. Multidrug resistant (MDR-TB) and extensively drug-resistant (XDR-TB) strains of *M. tuberculosis* are a growing clinical concern. These strains can arise due to misuse or mismanagement of antibiotic therapies. Therefore, it is imperative that proper multidrug protocols are used to treat these infections. Common antibiotics included in these mixtures are isoniazid, rifampin, ethambutol, and pyrazinamide.

A TB vaccine is available that is based on the so-called bacillus Calmette-Guérin (BCG) strain of *M. bovis* commonly found in cattle. In the United States, the BCG vaccine is only given to health-care workers and members of the military who are at risk of exposure to active cases of TB. It is used more broadly worldwide. Many individuals born in other countries have been vaccinated with BCG strain. BCG is used in many countries with a high prevalence of TB, to prevent childhood tuberculous meningitis and miliary disease.

The Mantoux tuberculin skin test is regularly used in the United States to screen for potential TB exposure. However, prior vaccinations with the BCG vaccine can cause false-positive results. Chest radiographs to detect Ghon complex formation are required, therefore, to confirm exposure.

These short animations discuss the infection strategies of *Mycobacterium tuberculosis*.

Figure 5 *In the infectious cycle of tuberculosis, the immune response of most infected individuals (approximately 90%) results in the formation of tubercles in which the infection is walled off.[11] The remainder will suffer progressive primary tuberculosis. The sequestered bacteria may be reactivated to form secondary tuberculosis in immunocompromised patients at a later time. (credit: modification of work by Centers for Disease Control and Prevention)*

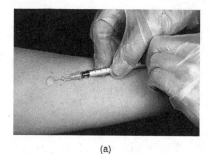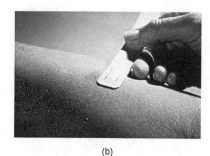

(a)   (b)

Figure 6 *(a) The Mantoux skin test for tuberculosis involves injecting the subject with tuberculin protein derivative. The injection should initially produce a raised wheal. (b) The test should be read in 48–72 hours. A positive result is indicated by redness, swelling, or hardness; the size of the responding region is measured to determine the final result. (credit a, b: modification of work by Centers for Disease Control and Prevention)*